# He Wondered *as* He Wandered

## Reflections *on* Birds, Butterflies, *and* Battles with Depression *from a* Marshland Naturalist

*In every walk with nature
one receives far more than he seeks.*

John Muir

# DAVID LORD

*Pageant Wagon Publishing
Vineland, New Jersey*

*He Wondered as He Wandered:*
*Reflections on Birds, Butterflies, and Battles with Depression from a Marshland Naturalist*
Written by David Lord
Compiled and Edited by Kathryn Ross

Copyright 2019, David and Catherine Lord

ISBN: 978-0-9910070-1-1

Pageant Wagon Publishing © 2005, 2017
A Division of Pageant Wagon Productions LLC
www.pageantwagonpublishing.com
info@pageantwagonpublishing.com

# Dedication
## To David Lord, Trail Angel

Fragile as butterfly wings
Harmonious as a songbird sings
Peaceful as the heavens above
I see you my brother, full of love
Seeking that calming space
Just to be in God's grace
There is no anger, there is no fear
Just relief in the tears
The paths are different
The destination the same
To shout from the heavens,
God's glorious name.
This we shall do because Jesus bled
See you again, my brother
At Heaven's trail head

Amanda Lord Wojcik

# Table of Contents

**EDITOR'S NOTE: Due to a format/print error, the pagination of the second half of this book is off by one page. Use this updated Table of Contents for this print edition. The error has been corrected for all future print-runs. We apologize for any inconvenience. Thank you.**

*He laughed easily and possessed a gift to make others laugh, which brought great joy to all.*

*The David and Cathy Lord Family*

# Foreword:
# A Word from the Family about David Lord
### By David and Catherine Lord

David Lord

The coolest person you will ever meet!

David, born on October 3, 1988, became the youngest member of the Lord family, with two much older sisters, Megan and Amanda, ready to spoil him. As a youngster, his easy-going manner delighted all who knew him. He laughed easily and possessed a gift to make others laugh, bringing great joy to all.

We owned a small farm in the Cape May, New Jersey area—a virtual playground for a curious little boy. Growing up immersed in farm life, his fascination with all creatures great and small found an outlet in the local 4H clubs. He raised three seeing eye puppies as one of his 4H projects. But the life and death realities of living on a farm heightened the sense of his own immortality and drew him to take hold of God. Early in his life, David understood that the loving God of such a beautiful Creation, created him simple and free. He knew Jesus was God's Son and his Savior, through whom he would live forever in the presence of God.

A voracious reader, David plunged himself into books about nature and sought out mentors to teach him more. He explored his world and retained information like an encyclopedia on a host of nature topics—especially birds and butterflies.

But, as he entered his early teens, he grew uncomfortable with himself when faced with new situations. Many times, he withdrew into a depression. His high school years presented new challenges and difficulties that he struggled to balance within himself. He continued to

1

withdraw when he felt uneasy in his surroundings, even though he was well-liked and possessed many loyal friends who served as a strong support group.

In his senior year at Cumberland Christian School in Vineland, New Jersey, he spoke at one of the weekly chapel services. He bravely took this opportunity to announce his struggles with depression and his attempts to commit suicide. A concerned teacher and counselor at the school told us of this alarming admission in his speech and suggested we seek professional counseling for David.

In our quest for help, we met immediate roadblocks. Facing challenges with David from this point would fill another a whole book, detailing all the ups and downs on the paths we traveled.

For instance, at the outset, it was difficult to get an appointment with a psychologist. We found they were acquired on a lottery basis. On a particular day, at midnight, we were instructed to call the doctor's phone number. The first fifteen callers would be registered as a new patient. If you missed the lottery you had to wait until the following month to try again for a chance to win a spot.

This was just one curve in the road as we learned first-hand the serious problems associated with securing adequate, professional help. As we waited for an opening to see a psychologist, our family doctor ordered anti-depressant medications to help David in the interim. Unfortunately, David had an allergic reaction to the prescription drugs and his depression worsened with increased anxiety and suicidal thoughts.

**There simply are not enough qualified doctors to meet the demand for hurting people and families struggling within the growing epidemic of mental health problems in our society and culture today.**

David pressed into his love for God and was baptized one summer at Camp Haluwasa. He served with the evangelism committee from the Methodist Church in Cape May Courthouse. Meeting on the boardwalk, Friday evenings in summer, he invited conversation with passersby asking the compelling question emblazoned on a large sandwishboard: "If you died tonight, would God let you into His heaven?" David's warmth, shy manner, respectful reserve, and intelligent words drew the hearts of strangers to him, willing to chat about eternity.

He graduated from Cumberland Christian High School in 2008, looking forward to starting classes at Lancaster Bible College that fall. His spot in the school's yearbook preserves his love and reliance on God knowing him in his need when he cites a favorite verse: *For the word of God is alive and powerful. It is sharper than the sharpest two-edged sword, cutting between soul and spirit, between joint and marrow. It exposes our innermost thoughts and desires.* Hebrews 4:12 NLT

But his favorite quote, "The story ends with me putting him in the wall," reminded his classmates of his keen sense of humor, while it revealed his resolve to win and beat the opponents in his life. It references a Geico television commercial (http://bit.ly/2NyO0HR) regarding a kid cousin of race car driver Mike Wallace being interviewed, making the claim that he will beat his famous adult nemesis be it with racing go-karts, shopping carts, or "those remote-controlled boats." With hilarious attitude and deadpan delivery—akin to David's own sense of humor—the kid plans to win at all costs, "putting him in the wall." That's the way David wanted the story to end, too.

He spent his summer working with Captain Bob on the Osprey Wetland Tours in Cape May, New Jersey, and performing with the Pageant Wagon Players in the *Old-Fashioned American Melodrama Summer Family Theatre,* where he had become an audience favorite in prior productions.

David also loved working with children through puppetry—be it in various children's church venues or passing on his love of birding to eager youngsters with Miss Kathy and *Tale Spin Stories* (refer to Introduction). He was trained by the interdenominational puppetry group Creative Ministries. After his passing, we donated David's extensive puppet collection to them, who in turn, donated the puppets to several churches in Cuba for use in children's ministries.

These were some of his favorite activities in his waning years of youth.

But, when September arrived and he started classes at Lancaster, he regressed. It was in this season that he composed *Diana's Song* as a thank you to one of his closest confidants, fellow Pageant Wagon Player Diana Hoffman, with whom he shared details of his inner struggles with depression and found her encouragement to be light in the darkness. It is included in this book.

As we prayed through the situation for a year and leaned into our Christian faith, the Lord led us to a Christian psychologist for counseling, Dr. Ronald Newman, who generously contributed Part Two of this book, focusing on depression and suicide awareness. Dr. Newman referred us to a neuroscientist who could do more testing using a holistic approach to wellness.

The first brain scan of David shocked us. We learned that his scans were worse than some of the Alzheimer's patients this doctor had treated. He developed customized supplements and holistic remedies specific to David's needs after testing. Thankfully, the new counseling and medicine regimen produced excellent results—an answer to prayer!

David's mental wellness improved. As long as he remained consistent with his medicines, he was balanced and able to function without battling inner torments. During this time, he took a sabbatical from higher education and devoted himself to advancing the mission of the Cape May County's Bird Observatory. He became a most sought-after guide on hundreds of wetland birding tours. During this time, he started a blog, *He Wondered as He Wandered,* as a place to collect and share his reflections on the marshland and wildlife he loved so well.

Perhaps this season of success gave him too much confidence. Perhaps he thought that he could continue on without the help of his supplements or doctor visits. In the end, he chose to stop relying on them in an effort to overcome without a crutch. His friends didn't need it. Why did he? After two years, he suspended the medicines and the doctors before returning to college to complete his education.

But on campus, new situations and environments triggered old torments to rise again. He persevered, fighting on his own. Each semester he changed his mind about what college to attend and what major to focus on. From pastor to psychologist to research lab scientist to mathematics professor, he changed schools and major/career choices regularly, while watching his close friends remain in their chosen fields of pursuit, achieve their goals, and launch confidently into their twenties.

For some reason, he never thought to pursue a career as a naturalist, even though he was already walking in aspects of that career, with great success, as a gifted amateur. He did not see it as a career path, so much as a home for escape and respite—something sacred, not to be sullied by the utility of a working life.

**He found the greatest solace and communion with God in the marsh and wilds of nature.**

He told us once that when he got out into the marshes the world was at peace and all his troubles faded away. Those places were like medicine to him. The counsel he received, the relationships he built, the respect he earned from connection with other kindred birders and naturalists, the lessons he learned through the observation of God's Creation, and the joy that filled his tender heart when he beheld the vast landscape of the marsh or an eagle on wing above in the sky, empowered him.

Perhaps, he thought, empowering enough to sustain him as he faced the task of higher education and career choices.

By his mid-twenties, in his final couple of years, his highs and lows caused him to engage life and withdraw from it in stark measures. On his last day, he shared Jesus and the love of God with his math tutor on the Rowan University campus. He prayed with her and returned home that evening overjoyed with the experience of touching someone's life for God. His delight lifted our hearts. But by morning on October 22, 2014, we knew the pain of his loss to his battle and his loss to us, as much as we understood heaven's gain.

**The grave could not hold Him, that's my King JESUS.**

Our family's purpose in publishing this book on the fifth anniversary of his passing is to let people know that there is a Light in the darkness, help for the hurting, and peace for the troubled soul in the Truth of the Word of God.

We want you to know that you are loved by the God of Creation. He created you to love Him and enjoy Him forever. Live your life to do just that.

David may have lost his battle with depression, but the war for his soul was won by Jesus Christ 2000 years ago. Jesus took David's sin upon Himself, because David couldn't pay the penalty for sin himself. Christ stood in David's stead before God the Father and paid the price for all sin through His death on the cross. But, because Jesus was God in the flesh, the grave could not hold Him. He had the power to conquer sin and death, rising from the dead to new life. Life He freely gives to us today.

If you are reading this book and facing problems in your life, please know that there is a God Who loves you and provides help in your time of need so you can have victory over the opponents in your life and—as David had once hoped to end his story—put them in the wall

Uniquely gifted with the powers of observation and retention of information, we watched David develop into the go-to-guide for getting the most out of birding tours and nature walks in our little neck of Southern New Jersey.

*Kathryn Ross*

# Introduction
## By Kathryn Ross

He had me in stitches the first time I saw him onstage. He played the title role in *The Importance of Being Earnest* during his sophomore year of high school. My husband Ed, and I, looked at each other by intermission and agreed. We were watching a re-boot of Steve Martin.

I knew he'd be a great asset to our Pageant Wagon Players Old-Fashioned American Melodrama theatrical troupe, entering our second of five summer seasons (2005-2009). I offered him a spot, on the spot. He became a featured performer and audience favorite in those shows, plus many other productions over the next six years. During those crazy fun days, Ed and I enjoyed watching him grow into a fine young man we called friend—and part of our family.

If you saw him performing onstage in one of the melodramas, you wouldn't be able to keep a dry eye for laughing. His comic genius seemed intuitive. But, his gift for comedic timing and slap-stick pratfalls was just a veneer for a serious young man possessed of a passion for God's creation in nature.

Uniquely gifted with the powers of observation and retention of information, we watched David develop into the go-to-guide for getting the most out of birding tours and nature walks in our little neck of Southern New Jersey.

This is why some of my favorite memories of David were not made on the stage—though those were plentiful—but in the wilds of the Pinelands, marshes, and Jersey shore waterways. In those pockets of Heaven on earth, he spent long hours studying nature up close and personal, specifically birds and butterflies.

Though I was the teacher and mentor, when we grabbed our binoculars and hiking boots, setting off for his favorite spots like Turkey Point and Bivalve in Cumberland County, and Cape May Point, we switched roles. I became the student.

David taught me how to listen and observe at a reflective level, making biblical truth and the character of God come alive in my spirit in fresh ways, with great delight. Ed and I began to take more time on our own walks to listen to the birds and be more curious about the wonders of nature beyond a surface fascination.

At our church where we shared many more adventures, he delighted the children and young families with his gift as a naturalist. Suddenly, everyone jumped on the bandwagon of bird watching. The little boys learned how to blow through their cupped hands to make bird calls. David was an excellent and patient teacher.

He collected and devoured information from books. Especially the classics. At the bookstore where my husband worked, David indulged his love for them. An avid reader, he often surveyed our home library making sure Ed knew his wish list, should we be getting rid of any books. We always sent him home with a treasure.

As a performance storyteller, I hosted a weekly story time at the Cumberland Mall in Vineland for seven years called Tale Spin Stories. When my story theme was birds, I invited David to come as a special guest with his birding equipment. The kids loved him. He enjoyed the gig so much that he came back for more: as a pirate, as a butler at a tea party, as a chicken, as the big bad wolf, as Beach Bum Bob, and even as Santa Claus!

David was very versatile.

I often refer to "my favorite day" being the birthday present he gave me one year—a butterfly tour of Cape May during the annual monarch migration. We wondered at the varieties of butterflies and dragonflies peppering the neighborhoods by the shore. David expertly named each one, explaining their peculiar characteristics. Afterwards, we enjoyed a nature walk through the marsh discovering various species of birds that, to my layman's eyes, remained hidden until he pointed them out to me.

Ed and I also enjoyed annual boat tours with David as our guide, noting the distinctions between falcons, osprey, vultures, and eagles soaring overhead in sapphire blue skies—not to mention the host of other bird life on the Maurice River shoreline flitting and frolicking about the water currents.

One evening we went in search of owls at Turkey Point. I heard their melodious calling, but never saw one. Even so, I stood amazed watching David carry on a conversation with them, mimicking spot-on owl calls. He even distinguished between the male and female calls in his response.

But above all, I loved hearing him share insights about God's creation. In the context of a litany of facts he'd whisper a concise line or two of spiritual connections to biblical truths regarding the flora and fauna we observed. I always returned home with meat for meditation and the task of further research on my own.

Imagine my delight when he announced the start of a blog titled, *I Wonder as I Wander*, to record his reflections. David's physical ears and eyes, finely tuned to the natural world, functioned as one with his spiritual ears and eyes. He translated what he heard and saw into compelling words, leading my heart deeper towards Christ.

I'll never forget the time we went to the annual Bay Days in Bivalve together—a June event. We walked out to the end of a long dock into the middle of the marsh. He surveyed the scene and sighed, his voice trailing off in a reverie. "I really love it out here . . ." he said.

For all I could see, David stood on the brink of an influential career as a naturalist, writer, and speaker.

Unfortunately, as much as he loved his moments soaking in the wonders of God in the marsh, sky, and shoreline, he battled the dark valleys of depression and doubt, unable to fully embrace his calling. As he grew through the teenage years into young adulthood, he set unrealistic standards for personal achievement in areas of study that did not match where God had gifted him. His brilliant, generous mind and heart wrestled with uncertainty.

After one of our nature tours seeing the eagles on the Maurice River, I made a little thank you card for him, including a quote by Vincent Van Gogh that I always thought fitting for him:

*Your profession is what you were put on earth to do with such passion and such intensity that it becomes spiritual in calling.*

*Vincent Van Gogh*

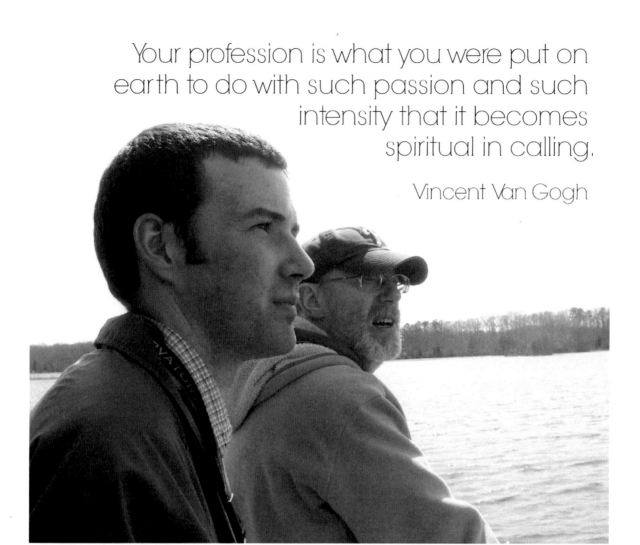

Tragically, on October 22, 2014, I received the news that David had lost his battle with depression. His untimely departure left a great void in the lives of so many. I don't think he ever grasped the full import of his influence upon the people he touched. His short 26 years proved him to be a doorway to good things and beauty—the go-to guide for finding God in the wilds of creation.

I cannot answer for the choice he made under the heavy burden he carried. But what he leaves behind is not a legacy of loss. It is a legacy of life.

In this collection of 32 reflective thoughts, *He Wondered as He Wandered: Reflections on Birds, Butterflies, and Battles with Depression from a Marshland Naturalist*, I've gleaned some of David's words as penned on his blog, *I Wonder as I Wander*, between 2011 and 2014. He published his last post three short months before he stepped into the presence of the God he loved. It is my hope that David Lord's legacy will increase through the print publication of his words, insights left behind in his writings, and the additional material generously donated by special contributors.

In **Part One: David's Journeys**, his birding buddy and school chum, Andrew Hughes, provides an introduction to David's nature trail observations. Four posts recount his thoughts while visiting two of his closest friends studying in England and France—Jon-Mark and Tim Grussenmeyer. Many thanks to Dr. Jon-Mark Grussenmeyer for providing the introduction to this section. Rounding out David's writings, friend and confidant, Diana Hoffman, shares her experiences walking with him on potholed pathways as the introduction to David's compelling short story written especially for her. It details the inner battle of voices luring a troubled heart to the brink of suicide—and the song that rescues in that place.

**Part Two: At the Intersection of Depression and Suicide** features valuable insights into the battlegrounds of depression and suicide from a professional counseling perspective. Pastor Russ Sterger worked closely with David in theatrical pursuits. He details their common battles and the connection he forged with David in a moving account penned four short months prior to losing his battle with cancer. David's pastor, Frank Ippolito, shares a powerful, encouraging message to lift hearts towards the light of goodness, beauty, and an understanding of deeper truths in David's legacy. And we are especially grateful for Dr. Ronald Newman's generous submission on suicide awareness featuring local resources to assist you or someone you love who may be battling issues in life that appear insurmountable.

David's sister, Amanda, family friends, respected peer enthusiasts at the Cape May Bird Observatory such as Peter Dunne, Pat Sutton, Deborah Shaw, and Robert Lubberman, lend personal tributes in **Part Three: Memories of David's Life and Legacy**. Featured here is a lyrical salute in song by singer/songwriter, Dawson Coyle, whom David mentored, often accompanying David on nature walks in search of elusive wonders with wings.

You'll learn more about the guest contributors to this book and all those who have made this project possible in the **Acknowledgements** section. The David and Catherine Lord family is thankful for all who have assisted in this work. All proceeds from the sales of this book benefit the NATIONAL SUICIDE PREVENTION LIFELINE, 1 800 273-8255. Visit them online at www.suicidepreventionlifeline.org.

## A Prayer for the Reader

David Lord possessed a unique mind, sharp intellect, tender heart, and keen gift of insight. Perhaps too unique, sharp, tender, and keen—making life a battle to balance.

He is greatly missed by those who have loved him. For me, though, he remains as close as the bird singing on the crepe myrtle branch outside my back window, the butterflies fluttering in the zinnia garden surrounding the front lamp-post, and the eagles soaring high out at Turkey Point when I make the time to revisit an old haunt and happy memory.

May the reflective thoughts culled together in this volume become a tour guide to inform your spirit and imagination, drawing you nearer to the Lord—wondering as you wander. In such a way, the Lord uses all things, bringing David's influential life to meet its full purpose—a legacy redeemed to the glory of God.

Kathryn Ross, Editor
October 2019

PART ONE:

David's
Journeys

He was a joy to know, and he impressed many with his ability to synthesize his nature discoveries with his knowledge of history, philosophy, and obscure television references.

*Pastor Andrew Hughes*

# Reflections of a Marshland Naturalist
**Introduction by Pastor Andrew Hughes**

It's December. The stars stretch their divine light through the darkness to reach the restless wanderers below. People come to Turkey Point to reciprocate the gesture. Behind me, the low mourn of a Great Horned Owl breaks the monotony of swaying reeds, teasing a smile from my face. She's calling from the same patch of woods where, a decade ago, I took David Lord and a few of our mutual friends on their first "Owl Prowl."

As we entered the woods, I described the expected species in that area and imitated their hooting and trilling calls for my patient companions. When someone takes you to an isolated forest after dark, it's best to accommodate their eccentricities. But David did more than tolerate our briar-filled slog through swampy woods, even when a wrong turn misplaced us for two hours. He came alive. A passion for the natural world captured him in its unyielding talons.

That weekend, we returned with the sun to the salt marshes, whose every denizen David would come to know and love. His attention to detail and encyclopedic memory made him a force to be reckoned with. He was a joy to know, and he impressed many with his ability to synthesize his nature discoveries with his knowledge of history, philosophy, and obscure television references. And, of course, his Christian faith.

Like David's own Lord, who reminds us to "look at the birds" as a living showcase of God's faithful provision (Matthew 6:25-27), David had a knack for seeing the Creator's truth embedded within His created world. The truth of the Scriptures came alive as he wandered through the treasure trove that is the Delaware Bayshore. In this collection of David's essays, we see a man both enthused by life and deeply haunted by its capriciousness. While this duality may surprise some readers, it fully coincides with the Christian worldview.

God made a good world and entrusted humanity to image His goodness and justice by, among other things, ruling over the natural realm and stewarding its resources wisely. But due to the sin in our hearts, we've utterly abused and neglected this mandate. Throughout these writings, we see David struggle with both the personal effects of sin—things like pride, lust, and avoidance of community support—as well as its corporate effects that many Christians overlook: environmental devastation, wastefulness, and unregulated habitat loss.

Perhaps more than most of us, David recognized that "the whole creation has been groaning" as it awaits a day when God fully restores order through His new creation. Jesus, the perfect King, defeated the spiritual powers that keep us from living harmoniously with others, ourselves, and God's good world. Together, we are invited to herald God's kingdom mission by trusting in Jesus' sacrifice as the means to "cleanse us from all unrighteousness" and advance His kingdom against both personal and corporate sin.

This royal victory gives every believer hope!

It's hope that, on his best days, David knew and felt and embodied for others. But even the brightest starlight takes time to reach us. In the meantime, we battle with loss, heartache, failure, and temptation, as we await the promised day of restoration.

That battle is entirely normative and should never be mistaken for a lack of faith, sincerity, or purpose. Even the Son of God experienced unanswered prayers (Luke 22:42), the pain of losing friends (John 11), and disgust at the damage caused by religious hypocrisy (Matthew 23). I'm convinced that those who are closest to God's heart will be similarly affected.

But this earthly struggle must also make room for an outworking of God's plan of blessing. We are welcome to mourn but must also remember that "all things work together for the good of those who love God (Romans 8:28)." This balance is as evident in David's essays as it was in his beautiful but tormented life.

I hope the following pages will inspire you to take a nature walk this week. If you need to grieve, then grieve. But remember that the pains of this world are only temporary, and that God is preparing something glorious for His children. Glimpses of His goodness can be found in every bird and tree and river. Listen closely with an open heart and mind. David will show you the way.

April 23, 2011

# Forest Fortress

*"A Mighty Fortress is our God,*
*A Bulwark Never Failing."*

The woods I stood alongside of seemed full of promise. Each square inch of understory appeared to creep with life; the life found only in those who wear feathers. My winged friends, however, elected to remain hidden from sight, only betraying their existence with auditory clues. Tiny "sips" and "cheeps" alerted me to their presence, but this morning that would not suffice; I must see these beauties.

Thankfully, a birder is not left alone when dealing with uncooperative avi-fauna. Birders have a tool, an aid that can make birds visible from thin air. This magic wand is called "pishing": a sound that imitates an angry Tufted Titmice. The usefulness of pishing is not obvious to most people. Making sounds at a tree or bush does not appear to be the height of productivity. People have the luxury of ignoring the sounds of riled Titmice. Birds do not.

Birds know that Titmice and Chickadees are pitbulls with wings. Whenever any type of danger approaches, these gray and white guardians faithfully spring into action. The whole forest will resound with "pishes," and any bird worth its salt will come to survey the situation and see what the danger is this time.

So, by imitating Titmice and Chickadees, a birder can easily pique the interest of other species of birds. What starts out as a few soloists voicing their protests may soon become a whole choir calling with unified umbrage.

Pishing: the reason I was making noise at a bush.

There! Movement! In the corner of my eye, the life I came here for. Pishing pulls through again.

The bird is a Hermit Thrush. A small, brown bird with a rusty tail and bold black belly spots, this unassuming bird is a common winter visitor in Southern New Jersey. Understated in just about every way, he lets you know he's near by a soft "chyk" and his distinctive motion of dropping his wings.

Subdued yes; stupid, no. For my Hermit Thrush did what any thinking bird would at a sign of danger. He went to the forest fortress: a green-briar bush.

Green-briar goes by a number of colloquial names: sticker bush, cat-paw, evil, etc. It is the classic thorn-bearing shrub, and it is unforgiving. I encountered green-briar on my first birding experience. A wall of it, in fact. I emerged from that natural edifice looking like a character from a Wes Craven film and have since learned to keep away from those ominous thorns.

But my friend the thrush learned to run to them. He freely and happily jumped into the midst of the bush. Pausing for a moment, he assessed the danger, and relaxed. He wasn't losing control. In fact, he had the freedom to look around, knowing his surroundings were the securest place possible. He was safe from the dangers that I alerted him to.

> The LORD is my light and my salvation—so why should I be afraid? The LORD is my fortress, protecting me from danger, so why should I tremble?
>
> Psalm 27:1 NLT

The world is continually sending out an alarm call. Its message is a cacophony of worry, despair and fear. We must respond with a soft "God is still on His throne; I am in Him." When the "wolves in sheep's clothing" come, we must rest in the Truth, for that is never shaken. When the darkness comes, we must remind it that it can never hurt us, for we are people of the light.

We must ever be learning just how mighty a fortress our God is.

# Pilgrims in the Dark

*Beloved, I beg you as sojourners and pilgrims . . .*

This past Easter morning beckoned me outside quite early. It was the silence that led me on. The pure, still, unadulterated silence of the night called me forth. I only followed because I was sure the silence would soon be broken.

Stepping out of my car, I embraced all the luminaries above, and felt their warmth and light wash every part of me. As I walked along, old friends such as the Scorpion and Cassiopeia gave their silent approbation for a tired, anxious mortal like me. For these heavenly lanterns knew I was there only to witness the silence being broken.

My thoughts rushed with excitement over the spectacular happening on the horizon. They ebbed and flowed against the shoreline of my grey matter, until only the future was on my mind. What if the future let me down? What if the silence wasn't broken tonight?

*SEEEEP*—The promised noise that broke the silence! What was it, you ask?

That seemingly insignificant sound was a nocturnal flight call of a migratory songbird. When songbirds migrate, they perform this vital function at night. They don't totally rely on their vision for this flight; instead they use such rudimentary tools as the earth's magnetic field, the position of the stars, and more physical elements of Creation. Employing these modes of travel allows them to fly at night, providing a safe cover for these tiny, feathered beasties.

However, when these birds travel together, the night can be a problem if you want to see your friend. It can also be a detriment if you happen to run into someone else—especially if that someone else is bigger than you. But perhaps the biggest danger of all is not keeping a steady course for your destination.

To combat all these potential perils is that tiny *SEEEP* mentioned above. These flight calls serve many vital functions. We process a few of these advantages through our brains, but if we had bird brains, I imagine the advantages of the flight call would be innumerable.

First, the flight call helps birds keep in touch. Without these tiny *SEEEPS*, birds would find themselves alone in the night sky. Not a comfortable place to be if you're heading from South America to Northern Canada, like some high mileage birds.

Second, the flight call keeps them safe. Should they receive a response from a bird ahead of them, look out!

But perhaps most importantly, keeping in touch with flight calls gets the bird to its destination in better shape, if at all. The life of each individual bird depends upon the flock as a whole. If I were a Blackpoll Warbler and I ended up in Russia instead of Ontario, I might be a little miffed at my friends for not letting me know I was on the wrong track.

As believers, we travel together in a dark environment, a world in which we have nothing. The Bible makes the emphatic claim that we are "sojourners and pilgrims" in this domain of darkness. We are simply foreigners on our way to our home country, passing through a hostile land.

That's why we vitally need fellowship: I used to feel the biblical command, "Do not forsake the assembly of believers," (Hebrews 10:24-25) was put forth simply to ruin my weekend. But as time performed its work, I found that fellowship was one of the most powerful weapons in my spiritual armory. Without communication, our soul weakens. Without fellowship, we will eventually put ourselves in our own little corner, where we will make daily sacrifices to our thoughts. The process is sad, but inevitable.

The road to heaven has many travelers, all with the same Book in their hands, and the same Spirit in their hearts. We must encounter them regularly, we must learn from the Book, we must fellowship. Or we may find ourselves in a place we had no intention of arriving at.

As I bid goodbye to my travelers in the sky that Easter Morning, I was filled with the joyful anticipation of celebrating that Holy Day with my fellow pilgrims. My heart was glad and expectant because of the fellowship ahead. I knew that as long as our feet were on the path, the book was in our hand, and the Spirit was in our hearts, we'd turn out fine.

But I also felt sorrow for those who would not be fellowshipping with their fellow Strangers that morning. My heart broke at the thought of solitude on such an important occasion. For a Christian without fellowship, is a *SEEEP* with no response.

April 30, 2011

# Lessons from a Chat

*The first shall be last, and the last shall be first . . .*

I slammed the brakes and nearly threw myself over the handlebars upon hearing his familiar song. He was back. After his winter break in Central America, my old friend had returned.

This comrade, a Yellow-breasted Chat is a large, gawky, pear-shaped bird that makes his home in shrub islands, and low dense thickets.

"How was your vacation?" I queried.

*WHOO, CH-CH-CH-CH*

Apparently, my question was not the icebreaker he was looking for.

"Was the weather to your liking?" I asked him, with piqued curiosity.

*GRRR CH-CH-CH-CH*

"Did you have trouble with your passport this time?"

*WHOOOOO CLK CLK*

My Chat had many secrets, but at that moment, he didn't seem too keen on giving any of them away. The Yellow-breasted Chat is an odd-ball among birds. Its distinctive vocalizations earned it the nickname Raucous Polyglot, meaning noisy many-tongued, in the 19th century. The bird has a bizarre musical taste as most of his calls consist of a whistle and a bit of chatter.

But the oddities don't stop with his voice. The bird's bright yellow breast and white "goggles" have earned it the nickname "clown-bird." This title seems to fit, as the Chat will often go into a bizarre display where it will skip from bush to bush, giving his raucous whistle and chatter all the way across. During these displays, he seems to break the laws of gravity by stopping in mid-flight, sinking toward the ground, and then picking himself up again, acting like the yo-yo of the gods.

Even his own family seems to think him something of an anomaly. He belongs to the Warbler clan, a group of small, musically talented, strikingly patterned songbirds. Compare a Chat to any of his smaller cousins and the differences are immediately apparent. Most Warblers are small and vibrant. The Chat is large and awkward. Most Warblers are superb songsters. The chat seems to be a reject from American Idol. Most Warblers are graceful fliers. The Chat makes you wonder how he gets from point A to point B.

"Yes, they broke the mold with you my friend," I said in the politest manner possible. "In fact, the world you inhabit seems totally up-side down," said my voice. *"Just like the world you inhabit,"* said my spirit.

As I looked at my friend, my mind's eye wandered. It raced back two-thousand years, when the Master sat on a mountain and gave a sermon that turned the world up-side down for everyone who had ears to hear. When we allow Christ into our hearts, he comes and gradually turns our perspective up-side down. He enters the doors of our souls with the keys to a unique Kingdom.

A Kingdom where the Master serves the servants. A Kingdom where death is necessary for life. A Kingdom where the malnourished orphan in India, raising her withered hand in praise, is as much an heir to riches as the CEO in New York City, raising his pen in a multi-million-dollar signature. The world would call such a Kingdom up-side down. Christ would call it reality.

I wonder how many Christians plan for Christ to turn this present-day world right-side up when they invite Him into their lives? I imagine we all have our own agendas for Jesus to fulfill. But gradually, our eyes are opened. When we look around, we see ourselves making the same mistake the crowds shouting Hosanna made. We find ourselves in desperate need of a divine shake-up.

Eventually, my mind wandered to the moment at hand and I found myself concentrated on my friend, the Chat. "Perhaps you and I have a good deal in common Mr. Chat," I said. He assented silently—quite a feat for such a noisy fellow. His golden moment of silence was followed by chatter and a few skips into a nearby bush, leaving only his voice behind.
"With the condition the world is in now, I think I feel much more secure in an up-side Kingdom, don't you?" I heard another pause. Then came his reply in those unmistakable tones: *WHOOO*—That's chat speak for "couldn't agree more."

# Bridges of Pinecones

Overcast. Chance of rain. It's the one condition that keeps normal people inside, watching T.V. or talking on the phone. The combination of grey sky and precipitation normally produces antagonistic feelings toward the outdoors.

Unless you're signed up to help run a booth at an Eco-Fair. Then the color of the sky and those pesky raindrops are moot points. Whether drought or monsoon, snowstorm or hurricane, you press on knowing you're fulfilling a higher purpose.

At this particular Eco-Fair, that higher purpose was simply assisting kids make Pinecone bird feeders. It's a simple concept: just dip the pinecone in peanut butter, roll it in birdseed, and there you have the perfect bird magnet. It's a simple trick that really connects kids with the natural world. Plus, there's a bonus—you've just made the world a better place for a lot of undernourished squirrels, too.

All through that gloomy, damp day, kids arrived, aligning themselves like an assembly line. Spread. Roll. Smile. Repeat.

This went on for a good hour or so before the assembly line broke down. Something got caught in a gear and the whole thing malfunctioned. There, right in front of our table was a gentle elderly lady, perhaps in her late seventies to early eighties.

Status Quo flew out through the window. The average age of the participants shot through the roof.

"I'll make a feeder, if you don't mind," intoned the thin vestiges of a whisper. I carefully selected a prime pinecone and handed it gently to this new volunteer.

Then, time froze—and seemed to backtrack. Taking hold of the timeless element of nature wrapped up a pinecone, those fragile, gossamer hands holding it transformed into what they were fifty years earlier. Sunshine rose upon wedding bells ringing loud and clear, scaring all the Pigeons out of the bell tower. Her ears once again heard the songs of birds singing solely for her as she held the hand of her newly betrothed.

But soon, the hands aged a little. She heard the cooing of Mourning Doves crying out as she threw dirt on a casket containing her true love.

The milestones of her life appeared to surface as soon as she held that pinecone. Touching a long familiar element of nature overwhelmed her with comfort and peace stirring memories of her life's joyous moments, traumatic moments, and those moments when words could not express the secret places in her soul. A bridge spanning over half a century was built in a matter of moments, merely by repeating a simple task she had probably done many times in years past.

However, the present burst rudely upon the scene, as it always does. Suddenly her hands aged and withered. Her hearing diminished. The sky was overcast again.

"Thank you," she quietly said as she walked away with her feeder and her ancient memories in tow.

For an instant, that woman built a bridge of pinecones to bygone days, across which flooded a host of wonderful memories ignited by a touch of nature. As she walked away, she drew a moment closer to crossing a new bridge to a place that would provide more enriching memories than had ever graced her aging mind.

# Ham, Caviar, and the Cure for Despair

*"O, God, my rock . . ."*

The sign stopped me in my tracks, taking my breath away in surprise: *"Our last day of operation will be June 18th."*

So read that cardboard obituary for my favorite deli on the face of the planet. Yes, America's Grim Reaper of an economy had stopped by for a visit in Greenwich, New Jersey, and took my favorite source of sustenance to the great beyond.

Walking into the deli was like stepping into a mausoleum—the air of death and despondency was palpable. The walls, which once held hundreds of pictures of happy people, were stripped bare, sending their cold, unfeeling aura throughout my being. My heart grieved, and I wondered: *"Where will I get my sandwich after those long, fatiguing bike rides? Where will I be able to get coffee on those cold winter mornings spent searching for eagles? What will I lean on?"*

A glimmer of life peaked through the bleak atmosphere as the owner stepped up to the counter.

"That's a real bummer about your deli closing," was the mournful commentary my mouth spat out with an air of despair.

"You've gotta do what you've gotta do," came the reply. Despite the casual air of defeat in her voice, her eyes asked a desperate question: *"What is there to lean on?"*

I took my ham and cheese sandwich and bicycled out to a favorite spot along the bayshore. This particular place is a location that has heard my joys and my sorrows expressed—a local landscape absorbing my joyful shouts and mournful cries. A place I could depend on. Or could I?

To the uninitiated, this precious place of mine is just a dirt road cutting through marshland. But a careful scrutiny of the wind that blows, the dust that flies, and the grass that waves will tell you all you need to know about the area's past.

This locale was known as Caviar, formerly a huge area for the exportation of—you guessed it—Caviar. The eggs of the Atlantic Sturgeon were shipped all over the world, and a good percentage of that supply came from this very spot.

Caviar was once a hot spot for industry. Closing your eyes, you could imagine the hustle and bustle of a booming town. Listen, and you'll hear wagons roll past on their way to

25

fortunes, while fishermen groan and curse as they ply their wares in exchange for immense amounts of money.

But open your eyes and you'll witness a tragic change. Gone are the industrious fishermen. Gone are the Sturgeon. Gone is the windfall of money. Instead of a prosperous community, you'll see a marsh stretching for miles and a bay that seems to have no end.

"I remember when you could walk to Delaware on the backs of Sturgeons," intoned a voice from behind me, interrupting my thoughts about the instability of life.

Turning, I found an old seadog attired in all of the expected apparel. He sported the classic overalls over a tan shirt. His eyes were deep and windburned. His pipe hung from his mouth, blending in with his bleach-blonde beard.

"Look, I'm sorry, I came up here to be alone." I tried to be as firm as I could, but my desire for solitude obviously bypassed his salty ears, as he came and stood alongside of me.

"Quite a few self-made millionaires came out of here," he said, not to anyone in particular. "I bet they thought those sturgeon would be choking up this bay forever."

"But we know better, right?" It was a feeble attempt at conversation, but my friend didn't seem to care.

"I would even wager that they thought this town would be here forever, too. In their mind's eye, they could see their deep pockets stretching for eternity. They probably thought that this industry would be the rock to lean on."

After this soliloquy, he sat, contemplated for several minutes, then added, "But I knew—" he caught himself. "—know better. Ain't nothing worse than depending on the wrong thing. That'll make you sick, every time."

We shared a moment of silence. A deafening silence. All the things I had leaned on in my life came roaring to the forefront of my mind: girlfriends, best friends, educational plans. You name it and I had probably put my trust in it at some point. Only after a short period of false security did I realize those things were false foundations. They were not and are not to be leaned upon with any confidence. Just like the industry that boomed and faded on the very spot my comrade and I found ourselves.

"Make you sick, every time," my friend mused, seemingly to the wind. "But I know there's more to this world than what meets the eye. I know where to build my foundation. And it ain't in no stinkin' money." He spoke with a violence I don't think I've ever witnessed. Then, as if to alleviate my fear, he chuckled. His chuckle evolved into a laugh, and then morphed into paroxysms of hysterical hilarity.

This tidal wave of jocularity lasted for about two minutes before it died down as quickly as it began. "Nope," he said, "you can't see my foundation, but it's the truest one ever."

I struggled to catch his drift. Perhaps he sensed this, as he got up and started to walk away.

"Will the bay ever know Sturgeon populations as it did two-hundred years ago?" I asked out of curiosity.

"Not likely," he responded with his back to me.

"Will my favorite deli ever open again?"

"If it does, it'll be run by a bunch of Sturgeon," he quipped, laughing again.

"Then what is there to lean on?" I asked out of sheer despair.

He turned and glanced at me. In his stoic eyes I found the only acceptable answer to such a vital question.

Jesus.

The Rock that stands throughout Eternity.

. . . on that gray morning . . . no thoughts
were further from my mind than those
of anxiety and dread.
For I had a guide.

From *Into the Wild Gray Yonder*

# Into the Wild Gray Yonder

*Give up your selfish ambitions . . . Follow me.*

The fog grew thick and heavy. The waterway we traversed became quickly inundated with a dense, gray shroud.

- Our activity: kayaking.
- Our location: Cape May, New Jersey
- Our surroundings: Well, we couldn't see them.

Heavy fogs around Cape May, common occurrences in spring and early summer, find their origins over the Atlantic Ocean. Despite SPRING boldly displayed on the calendar, old man winter still has his icy grips on the ocean temperature, often keeping it around 50 degrees Fahrenheit, even into early June.

When an East wind comes along, that icy chill comes off the ocean and onto the land. Once the cold air meets its warm, humid counterpart on shore, a heavy mist is produced, and the result can be awe-inspiring. But if you're up a certain creek when the fog rolls in, even the proverbial paddle won't help you much.

Fog has the effect of letting you only see what is immediately ahead of you. A person in fog finds himself in a bubble—an isolated area that only gives enough visibility to move forward.

If I were alone in my kayaking venture, I would not be ashamed of the fearful, anxious thoughts occupying my mind. Terror would be a natural and appropriate response to such an experience. Going solo in this way would rightly infuse each turn with a sense of dread—every step of the journey becoming a source of restlessness.

But these feelings did not concern me on that gray morning. In fact, no thoughts were further from my mind than those of anxiety and dread.

For I had a guide. A friend who had kayaked that creek many times before. My kayaking brother was familiar with all the ins and outs of the way we were going.

And I had an extra reason to be confident in my mentor: he lived on the creek. In fact, from his house, he could observe the area from every angle. My trust in him was founded in the unmatched knowledge he possessed.

Because of my leader, I could paddle freely, peaceably enjoying every moment. Every stroke, every ripple in the creek, every drop of water that fell from my paddle—all of these things were mine to cherish in peace. A guide paddled alongside me and would see me safely to my destination.

The parallels between my trip up the creek and pilgrimage through life sprang to mind with an unearthly vibrancy. I thought back to moments when I wanted control over where I was going. I remembered those times when I thought I was the master of my destiny, when I thought my plans would lead me on. Only to find those plans led to dead ends.

Through a biblical re-education, I discovered that moments of self-confidence are redeemed through an unwavering trust in the Lord. However, it would be a deception to put forth trust in the Lord as a simple, easy task. To do so insults the fight of faith, a slur against the lives led by the Heroes of the Faith.

In an era when humans seem to want everything on-demand—immediate gratification—belief in an invisible Deity seems ludicrous. Especially believing in His control of the future. The idea of trusting in the Lord is nonsense in a culture abundant with independent, self-made, and strong-willed individuals.

And so, the fight begins for the Christian. It is the struggle to live counter-culturally. Each morning, we must take up the shield of faith. Every evening, we must remind ourselves that God is on his Eternal Throne. Every moment, we must fight to lose control.

This is not optional, as those who come to God *"must believe that He exists, and that He rewards those diligently seek Him"* (Hebrews 11:6). As we build our faith in God, we gradually lose our trust in our own plans. And as control slowly slips from our hands, we find a Friend who has the best perspective on life—seeing all things from all angles: past, present, and future. We encounter a Shepherd who takes great joy in giving us the Kingdom. We find a Guide who navigates us through this foggy world, step by step, precept by precept, until His plans are fulfilled. Believe it, or not.

# On the Majesty of Change

The water rushed down the rocks with alarming force, creating a reverent atmosphere. A waterfall? In New Jersey?

Though nothing in size compared to major waterfalls, this majestic sight was foreign to my experience. No landscape in my neck of New Jersey has the privilege of being adorned with a waterfall, but these scene-stealers frequently grace the ridges of the Northern region of the state.

My soul filled with awe at such a tremendous sight. My mind raced with words describing this unreal visage. Such majesty. Such dominion. Such force. Such change.

Change. That's the verbiage that best describes a waterfall. Change is a word that covers all aspects of a waterfall's nature: past, present, future. I wondered what the falls looked like when the Native Americans roamed freely through this beautiful area. I couldn't help but imagine the waterfall as a pristine, solid rockface, slowly starting to feel the changing presence of that first small trickle of water.

I wondered how the surroundings would appear fifty years into the future. What rocks would still be standing? Which stones would be ground to a fine, powdery mix?

No matter what the starting point for the waterfall, and no matter its ending place, the area would be in a constant state of change because of the powerful waterway that made the rocks its home. Status Quo means nothing when rushing waters take hold of an area. It will always know change.

To some, the idea of change is repugnant. The very notion of a shake-up in a well-ordered routine is enough to cause heart-failure for some people. *"Why mess with perfection?"* they reason, as their days rip away with an eerie sameness.

At one point in my life, I reasoned along those lines as well. I was the posterchild for invariability. I remained in this immutable state until I let the river of the Holy Spirit have its way in my life.

Then the changes came with alarming frequency.

The concept of change is well represented in the Bible. A Creator looks at His recently fallen creations and waits for the day when He can change their hearts permanently, restoring His precious fellowship with them. An obedient family waits in an ark for the waters to recede, with no idea what they'll find once this new world is theirs. Frightened disciples wait in an upper room for the Holy Spirit, a gift that would change them from fearful followers to bold believers.

The frequency and examples of change in Scripture is a constant. To deny it is to deny the Christian experience itself. Change for a person without Christ can, and should, be frightening. Without the Rock of Ages as a firm foundation, life can seem nothing more than quicksand, ready to suck a person down with each thrashing step.

But for the believer in Christ, change is an exciting and dynamic prospect. The Christian can lift his head up high, and march boldly into a transforming situation, fully aware that the change is an outpouring of God's love.

In fact, change gives a Christian hope because change affirms the constancy of God: *"While the earth remains, seedtime and harvest, and cold and heat, and summer and winter, and day and night shall not cease,"* (Genesis 8:22 NKJV). *"He who has begun a good work in you will complete it until the day of Jesus Christ;"* (Philippians 1:6 NKJV). Whenever change is witnessed, whether in nature or in our personal lives, we know an unchanging God is orchestrating each circumstance for His glory.

Staring at the waterfall, I couldn't help but be awed at the magnificent changes that water can produce. The Native Americans who once knew this land so well would be stunned to see the waterfall as it is today. In fifty years, the river may make this area unfamiliar to my eyes. As long as that river has its way, change will occur.

Looking inward, I saw a young man, ripe with trepidation at the big changes that loomed on the horizon. The fear of the unknown effects of each alteration struck chords of terror in the unknown regions of his heart. Everything said to run. Run from the changes. Run from the horizons.

However, those thoughts of escape were overtaken by thoughts of a loving Father—a spiritual Guardian who knew the changes this young man—my fearful self—would face from before the foundation of the world.

I thought about a Son—a Heavenly brother whose appearance I am changing into every day. I thought of the Holy Spirit—a River of Living Water that sees me transformed into a new creation; an agent of change renewing me daily.

The thought that this Godhead was instituting each change in my life is a comfort beyond words. Instead of running from the changes, I run towards them, with arms wide open. Lifting my Spirit toward Heaven, I commit each change into the hands of an all-knowing God and let the River flow.

No wonder they're called Pitfall Traps . . .
If you don't inspect the flower, you can't fall
in the juices. You've got to nip the problem
in the bud, no pun intended.

From *Pitfalls*

# Pitfalls

"This was worth the hike," I managed to wheeze out through gulping breaths once we'd reached the apex. Before us lay an intriguingly mysterious habitat—a chunk of natural wonder I'd never experienced before.

"Boreal Bog," said my hiking comrade, James. "A change from the saltmarsh, eh?"

Though I will never lose my passion for those waving acres of grass found along the Delaware Bayshore, I found myself strangely fixed on this new, foreign terrain. "Looks like we're on another planet," I finally said, after a bit of searching for the right words.

The term boreal refers to the high northern reaches of the globe. The Canadian portion of this pristine habitat reaches its southern edge in our northern states, making for an invaluable addition to the diverse tapestry of the North American landscape.

I ran my eyes over this alien area, searching high and low for new discoveries to catch my attention. Finishing my visual survey, I looked down at my feet, only to find my greatest discovery yet: Pitcher Plant! "James, LOOK, LOOK! PITCHER PLANT!" My incessant exclamations and directional pointer finger left no doubt as to the vicinity of my glorious find.

My travelling partner couldn't hide the look of confusion on his face. I had just traveled ten hours to be enthralled by a plant I could have found five minutes away from my house.

No matter where you find this distinctive plant, the surprise and wonder of it never ceases. Pitcher Plants are carnivorous plants, wanting nothing more than to feast on unsuspecting flies. Combining their colors with the false promise of nectar, these deadly beauties catch insects off guard. Once the potential victim has inspected his potential feeding trough, he takes a final leap into certain doom. Once inside the lowest part of the plant, the part with the nectar, fine hairs prevent the bug from ever going up again, entrapping him in a gooey mess. Juices absorb the insect's body until the plant has digested the entire meal, ready to dine on the next poor traveler hoping for a bite to eat.

"Amazing things, eh?" my friend unemotionally intoned. "No wonder they're called Pitfall Traps.

*"Pitfall. Pitfall. Pitfall."* My mind sounded like a broken record, mulling over this crucial noun in the Christian's vocabulary.

"And to think, this bog is just full of them," James finished, taking another survey of the extensive swamp.

And he was right. The clumps of pitcher plants weren't obvious, but upon closer inspection, the bog was littered with those deadly beauties. "I sometimes feel like those flies crossing this bog," I muttered, fixing my eyes on a particularly large clumps of plants.

"How so?" James asked, lifting an eyebrow in curiosity.

"I feel like my voyage through life is full of pitfalls. As soon as I think I'm past a particular problem in my relationship with God, I walk a little further, look a little closer, and there's the pitfall again! And most of the time, I hardly know they're coming."

James sat for a little, contemplating something. Whether it was the bog, my speech, or peace in the Middle East, I couldn't say. I usually gravitate toward friends who are deep into their well. James was no exception.

I continued. "Take, for instance, pride. I thought my problems with pride were things of the past, in the rear-view mirror. But then, I suddenly find myself entertaining haughty thoughts, things that seem to run straight against the will of God."

A contemplative "hmmm" was all the response I got. I went on. "I feel like those flies because I seem to be sucked dry of all that spiritual strength I once enjoyed, just like those poor insects who have no way of escape."

I sat, winded from my speech, staring at my stoic mentor. Eventually, he turned to me, and with all the common sense in the world, blurted out, "Stop it."

"Excuse me?" I asked, suddenly on the defensive.

"If you're dealing with pride, stop the thought in your mind. Tell yourself to 'stop it' as soon as the idea forms in your head."

"I don't understand." I stammered, taken back by the frankness of my companion.

"If you don't inspect the flower, you can't fall in the juices. You've got to nip the problem in the bud, (no pun intended)." With this final admonition, James fell back to contemplating the Boreal Bog, and all the other secrets it held.

I sat stunned. Those spiritual traps I grieved over so often could've been avoided had I stopped it. In all those black times when I felt my soul being eaten away by spiritual acids, I've always had a Father standing by saying, "When you've stopped it, why not ask for my Spirit to fill the empty space in your thought-life?"

To be sure, I'm thoroughly equipped to lead a victorious Christian life. All I have to do is unite God's plan with my will, and I'm prepared for every fiery dart that comes my way. Surrendering my will to God is a crucial step toward victory.

"I have overwhelming victory through Christ!" Just another message hidden in nature from the Creator. Just another silent corner of creation speaking a word so loud it could destroy the gates of Hell.

"Well," I said, after chewing these instructions over in my mind, "ready for breakfast? I've made fly sausage!"

A smile spread across the stoic countenance of my friend. With that, we started down the mountain, leaving a bog full of pitfalls well behind.

Cape May Point State Park, an awe-inspiring marshland abutting the Atlantic Ocean. It is an area rife with joy.

From *Cape May Point State Park*

June 23, 2011

# Cape May Point State Park

John Denver once said he loved to "share the joy that he found in living." I suppose if that's the only thing the preacher can say about me at my funeral, it will be sufficient.

And so, let me introduce you to a wonderful area known as Cape May Point State Park, an awe-inspiring marshland abutting the Atlantic Ocean. It is an area rife with joy. This past Tuesday (Summer Solstice) I found myself wandering through the marshes and dunes of this diverse habitat, simply observing. Simply shrinking away from the madding crowd and getting close to the dust from which I was made.

What did I see? I'll let that speak for itself:

This Great Egret was hunting Bunker Pond with all diligence. Great Egrets tend to be quite languid in their pursuit of fish and frogs and such. But when they strike, those sharp bills can do some damage.

Here's the Great Egret's little cousin, the Snowy Egret. He's much more frantic when foraging than his relative and a lot of fun to watch as a result. He has bright yellow feet, which he often uses to imitate worms, luring unsuspecting prey to the surface.

I saw this frontal view of a snag (dead tree) occupied by young Barn Swallows. These guys were anxiously expecting Mama to come with a fresh bug, alerting me to her presence with excited chatter.

This little beauty is my all-time favorite butterfly: the American Copper. The Coppers like to lay their eggs in certain types of grasses and can be found in abundance in localized areas. I had a friend count over 200 individuals in one field! The more the merrier, I say.

Here's the same bug with his underside showing. I made sure he was fined for indecent exposure.

This is a Little Wood-Satyr butterfly. His cryptic colors come in very handy against the hungry avian occupants of the park.

Here's one of the Bluette Damselflies. Damselflies are similar to Dragonflies, but are generally much smaller, with their wings closed behind their backs. This little fellow was only slightly thicker than a pin.

But for all the beauty in the world, there must be bullies. Here are two Fish Crows. These birds are a nuisance because they've developed an appetite for the endangered Piping Plover that nest on the beach at the park. They should really stick to Cicadas.

The most elegant, but also the most problematic, bird I saw would have to be the Mute Swan. Mute Swans are non-natives, having been introduced for aesthetic purposes about 200 years ago. They are aggressive, often killing the other inhabitants of the ponds they frequent. They are destructive, pulling up the vegetation by the roots, instead of clipping it, a feeding style that eventually sterilizes an area. And perhaps most importantly, they're dangerous, having been known to break the legs of unwary passersby.

Lastly, here's my friend the Red-winged Blackbird inviting you back.

*Photo Credit: Red-winged Blackbird photo by Kevin Karlson*

# Saints and the Salt Marsh

In all my years as a tour guide, I have never failed to see a look of wonder cross the faces of my patrons as they gaze upon the beauty of the Atlantic Coastal Salt Marsh.

The salt marsh eco-system is a vitally important piece of our natural landscape. If you live in New Jersey and have ever driven down the Garden State Parkway and see wide-open plains that resemble prairie lands, those are salt marshes.

The salt marsh performs a number of crucial services for the well-being of wildlife and humans alike. These waving acres of grass are the nurseries for most of the major fish species that we find on our dinner tables. That striped bass you enjoyed for dinner last night most likely entered the universe via one of our local salt marshes.

Though these areas can appear calm at times, a violent circle of life is revolving just below the surface. To begin with, the grasses of the salt marsh are very important for certain types of fish.

Every time a tide recedes, it takes with it nutrients collected from the grasses. These microscopic meals are gobbled up by the numerous varieties of filter feeding fish that call the salt marsh home. As soon as those on the bottom of the food chain are satisfied, the bigger fish feast on them—only to find themselves eaten by the hungry birds that hunt the salt marsh.

The circle of life is red in tooth and claw.

But perhaps the most intriguing aspect of these unique areas is the way they expand. Salt marshes are dominated by the annual grass *Spartina Alternaflora*, a plant that dies back each winter and decomposes. As the roots start their slow recycling process, a new layer of sediment is formed. This is no muddy, silty foundation but a firm, solid ground that you can drive a car over. And trust me, I've had my car in it, and it's heavy duty stuff. (Though I'm not paying for your tow truck if you try it with a MAC truck.)

Death making all things solid.

When I think on the composition of this favorite habitat of mine, my mind wanders to the Martyrs of the Christian faith.

What courage it must take to face the final enemy in the name of your ultimate Friend.

What heights of faith, what depths of love must be required to die for what you believe.

I think of Stephen, the faithful one who set the precedent for the acceptance of martyrdom. I think of Peter, hanging upside down on a cross. Of John, boiled in oil.

Fast forwarding through time, I think of the great European theologians who chose to die to themselves, so that we might have a true understanding of what God's Word says. Wycliffe, Luther, Zwingli—great men all, who suffered persecution, dying to themselves so I could have the firm foundation of the Word of God to stand on.

The story of the true Church has not been a peaceful one. It is a saga drenched in the blood of those who chose to emulate their Master.

When I look at a salt marsh now, a parallel portion of my brain kicks into gear, ruminating on the Christian life. I see life everywhere. Activity is the common denominator, a constant undercurrent, whether in a marsh or a body of believers.

But I also look upon the landscape in a somber reverence, fully aware that we are called to leave a solid foundation for the feet of future believers to firmly stand on.

Fully aware that it may take dying to keep the legacy alive.

## Simple

"I hope you've found something special that's worth sitting on the ground for." The voice broke my concentration. My perfectly aligned camera lens shifted a fraction of an inch.

The inquiry was perfectly natural. There I was in the middle of a State Park, flat on my belly, with my camera pointed at a few dead leaves.

"Oh, I've found something worth crawling on my belly for," I responded, half focused on the conversation, half focused on the object of my attention.

"What's that?" the curious woman asked, straining to catch a glimpse of the thing that consumed my vision.

Experienced in the fine art of pointing out small insects, I stood and positioned the shadow of my finger so that it pointed directly at the desired object.

There on the soft Cape May sand was an American Copper. An insect so magnificent it has earned a place in my heart as my favorite butterfly. But what it possesses in charm it lacks in scope, being about the same size as my thumbnail.

The intruder of my serene moment looked bewildered, giving the impression that she didn't see the attraction.

"Here, take a look-see on my camera," I said, displaying the picture I had taken before she came along.

"Wow," she exclaimed, spurred on by the simple elegance of this small creature.

Why do I hold the American Copper in such high regard? It's a fair question. Do I admire it because of its vibrant colors? Probably not. A Copper among a group of sub-tropical butterflies would surely fade into the background.

Do I appreciate this critter due to its hardiness? Nope. For the most part, a butterfly's life is as transient as a summer cloud. Its predatory skills? No. Its ability to fly long distances? Maybe. Its adroitness at balancing budgets? He could be worse.

As I ruminate upon the Copper's existence, I feel a certain respect for its simplicity. Humanity today has little room for the simple. The woman at the park, when invited for a closer view, became an exception to the majority. In my experience, most would just pass by the extravagantly simple, preferring less of the elegant, elemental qualities of life.

As for me, simple pleasures hold charms that keep calling me back. A bike ride through a small town. Watching a mama bird feed her young. Listening to the sound of people laughing. These are the moments that captivate my attention.

Even so, I often wonder how many small blessings I pass by as I look ahead for those loud, large gifts I expect on the horizon any day. It's alarming to contemplate the sweet, simple memory-makers I have run by on the road on the way to the bigger, brighter things I feel God owes me. How often have I missed gifts at my feet when my eyes are fixed straight ahead, looking into the distance, wondering what's next?

My impromptu companion and I stood silent, each finding something different in this marvelous creature to revere.

"Good thing you were here, or I'd have missed it," the Copper's new admirer admitted.

"Simple, isn't it?" I smiled and got back on the ground to admire the beauty of the basic, once again.

# Fourth of July

*Deadly. That's the word to describe him. Deadly.*

*He treads the water, searching for unsuspecting fish to dine on. His eyes search the marshes and bays, hoping for the right meal at the right time. Once his sight locks onto his potential food-stuff, he stares. With all the patience in the world, he stares his prey down, positioned as still as the marsh grass landscape he hunts against.*

*Then, when it seems an eternity has passed, he senses the moment—that ripe period of time when he can strike. Raising his dagger-thin bill, he rapidly plunges his head into the water, emerging triumphant in his hunt for a meal.*

This dramatic little monologue is a good description of my friend, the Tri-colored Heron. This multi-colored marsh beauty is a stunning example of the variety of life the bird world presents us with. His long, thin neck and bill truly set him apart in the realm of heronry. (I just made that word up.)

Not only is he distinctive, he's also germane for the fast approaching 4th of July holiday. Why? Because he's red, white and blue.

That's right, with a reddish cast to the neck (especially as a juvenile), a stark white belly, and greenish-blue back, the Tri-colored Heron is a truly patriotic bird.

America was once the Tri-colored Heron, at least that's what they tell me. Just as that feathered fisherman is the thinnest of the Heron family, so our great country was lean, trim and fit. We once had the power to free ourselves, the urge to free others, and the discipline to maintain freedom.

We were also noteworthy, just like the Tri-colored. Big, bold, flashy, we were the ones that other nations looked to for inspiration. Like ancient Rome, we sent our influences far and wide throughout different lands. We were ubiquitous. We were abundant.

But blink, and suddenly a change has occurred. Suddenly the lean, fit empire has become soft and flabby. In a short manner, our orderly, regulated world has erupted in a chaotic fashion. In an instant, we find ourselves on the attack from within and without. That proud, global bulldog has awoken to find his house on fire, and his yard flooded.

Who could possibly have the answer to these exigencies? What solution could turn an up-side-down world right-side-up?

I think my friend with the deadly aim and the coat of many colors may have an answer. Oh, he may not be *the* answer, but with his needle-like bill, he is pointing straight at the answer.

> *For ever since the world was created, people have seen the earth and sky. Through everything God made, they can clearly see his invisible qualities—his eternal power and divine nature. So they have no excuse for not knowing God.*
>
> Romans 1:20 NLT

Our world searches for answers with unprecedented fervor. All nations and peoples are caught up in frantic straits, seeking solutions that just don't materialize. Ours is a planet populace refusing to turn and see the world through the eyes of its Creator.

Meanwhile, creation is forever pointing upward in hopes that, one day, humanity will come to its senses and turn to its Creator.

That is, perhaps, the greatest secret my friend the Tri-colored Heron knows.

But he's only a sign-post on the journey home.

July 5,2011

## The Arizona Trilogy—Part 1
# Bloodshed at the Blood-bought Corral

*As you read on here, as I open the doors to the memory bank of my mind, you may feel the hot, dry desert winds start to blow. You may hear the low murmurs of free-range cattle. If you're lucky, you may even glimpse a road-runner speeding by.*

*All these sensations emanate from a wonderful birding excursion I took to Arizona in May of 2009. Arizona is a natural wonderland and a highly favored spot among birders, due to its predilection to attract Mexican species of birds across the border (Birders Without Borders).*

*In honor of that wonderful entry in my data bank, I want to pen a trilogy of reflections, inspired by the Grand Canyon state itself. Here's a fine bit of fiction on the deadliest enemy known to man, in one of the deadliest towns in the old west: Tombstone, Arizona.*

Though the music was blasting from the Birdcage Saloon, Christian would not be distracted from his purpose. He had come out to the Blood-Bought Corral to fight his enemy: Sin.

"You know what to expect," he said, addressing himself while rubbing his ill-shaven face. "Big, bold, and deadly." He described his enemy well based on his previous encounters with those transgressions that so easily tripped him up before. "Yep, Lust, Murder, Theft—things too big to slip out from under my watchful eye."

He winced with each mental reference to his previous life mistakes. He was here to make sure those mistakes were at an end.

*Psst . . .* came a low hiss from behind a few barrels.

Christian stood taut at attention. Could this finally be his foe revealing himself?

*Psst . . .* came the same invitation, again—this time from another part of the corral.

His mind raced. His heart, palpitating wildly.

Suddenly, the atmosphere filled with "*pssts*," polluting the airwaves to such a degree that even the bawdy tune from the Birdcage was drowned out.

By now, Christian's heart beat in fear as his eyes filled with a fiery rage.

"Christian," spoke a voice he didn't recognize.

"I'm here," he replied, with all the defiance he could muster.

"Here to play, are you?" the voice taunted, full of malice.

"I'm here to win a battle," Christian said, summoning courage from the deepest parts of his being.

"Hmmm," the voice sounded doubtful and found form, when, from behind the barrels emerged a well-dressed, well-groomed, respectable looking man. His sharp-shooter apparel shimmered in the noon-day sun. When he opened his mouth, a row of brilliant teeth invited admiration. "Victory, eh?" The man calmly inspected his slim, keenly polished gun, keeping Christian in his line of sight at the same time.

"The victory is in hand," announced Christian, regaining his shaken composure. "I'm already a victor through—"

"Through whom?" the sharp-shooter cut in. "Who wins your victories?

"Christ—"

"—ian?" The well-groomed one smirked, swiftly cutting off Christian's reply.

"What do you mean?" Christian growled.

"You were going to attribute your victories to Christ," the slim man said, a fierce look crossing his face at the mention of the Name. "You . . . you . . ." he stuttered, "You were going to let all the glory go . . . there . . ." he pointed upward. "But we all know the glory should go . . . THERE!" A crooked finger pointed accusingly at Christian.

"No!" Christian objected.

"Yes," the man rebutted. "Fair is fair. You know, you're the talk of the town."

"Why?"

"The way you handle that gun, is simply . . . amazing," the stranger said, seeming to struggle in the search of an appropriate adjective.

"Really? I'm famous?" Christian's voice cracked in hesitation.

"Oh yes, my friend." The stranger circled Christian like a vulture eyeing his next meal. "The way you slaughtered Lust was superb."

"Really?" Christian perked up at the compliment.

"More than superb. Fantastic!" The man grinned like a Cheshire cat, his face growing larger with each note of praise. "And no one has *ever* seen Lying go down so fast."

"Really," Christian said with more confidence.

"Yes, you . . . are . . . the . . . victor!" The man grinned wider and wider until his eyes squeezed tight together.

"Yes. I am. I'm so glad someone noticed.  My name isn't recognized enough, I know. You encourage me, sir. I've got a whole new outlook because of you Mister . . . Mister . . ." Christian looked closely at the man. "What's your name?"

"Pride."

Christian froze. He had heard of Pride and was aware of his expertise at winning gunfights. Tiny beads of sweat formed on Christian's brow. His nerves wrestled with thoughts of fight or flight—settling on Anger, instead.

"Oh, don't worry about me." Pride responded. "I'm not a really big Sin, like Lust or Drunkenness." Pride momentarily turned his back and felt something hard against his spine. Christian had taken advantage of the instant necessary to pull his gun. Pride set his teeth on edge and grimaced in measured response, "In fact, most people don't even know I'm there."

Christian refused to come this far and lose the battle. "You're done, Pride!" he screamed. The music in the Birdcage abruptly stopped. Christian's declaration drew the townsfolk into the street, curious to see what was happening.

"Oh, come on," Pride coolly coaxed. "Who gets hurt by pride? Pride's not such a big deal."

*Pride's not such a big deal.* The words struck Christian to his heart. He looked to himself. To the crowd. He looked everywhere in those few key seconds—except up. "Pride's not . . . such a big deal," Christian muttered mechanically. Weakened, he dropped his gun.

*Bang.*

In the blink of an eye, Pride shot Christian.

"No. I'm not so big." Pride sneered and fired another shot into the downed Christian. "I'm only the reason there's a Hell."

Christian gasped in pain as Pride delivered a swift kick to his stomach.

"I only caused God's greatest treasure—humanity—thousands of years of turmoil and suffering and mayhem." Another kick. "But no. I'm no big deal."

With one final thrust of his foot to his downed opponent, Pride grinned his sleaziest grin. He bowed to the onlookers and disappeared.

A bruised Christian remained in the corral writhing in his loss but enriched in a painful tutorial. A lesson that gave him a new-found reason to LOOK UP when Pride comes to town.

The Arizona Trilogy—Part 2
# In the Valley of the Shadow

My eyes developed a personality disorder. They longed with all their might to look up but knew that looking down was best for the journey ahead.

Up, Up, Up. That's where you'll find it. Up there.

My target was the Common Black-hawk, a creature that looks as if God took a lump of coal and carved a bird out of it. This black beauty primarily breeds in Central and South America, but inches his range into the North America with small territories in the Southwestern United States. It is one of the prolific number of trans-continental bird species that send new birders into fits of passion when visiting Arizona.

My hiking party and I found ourselves traversing rocky, wet, terrain in search of this birding Mecca. The area we were scouring goes by the name of Aravaipa Canyon and has been the last trail that many good pairs of sneakers have seen. Between the spiky, rocky terrain, and the river that must be passed through, Aravaipa has been the ruin of walking shoes for many unwary tourists.

Where are all the tourists? Oh, that's right, limited access. I'm okay with that. I still have trouble deciding which was more appealing: the fact that a rare North American bird called this canyon home, or the fact that the Nature Conservancy has a limit of fifty people per day. In the end, I found the sum of a desirable bird and the lack of crowds to be a winning combination.

If I didn't find this bird, I would emerge from this hike a loser. With this in mind, we pressed on, looking for this treasure with feathers.

I had collected all the information I could before starting the trek. I knew to check along the river's edge and to look for the flashy white bands on the tail. But I especially concentrated my studies on the call. Armed with this knowledge, I set out boldly in the quest for the Common Black-hawk, leading my party with great hope.

Even so, if you knew every detail ever known about the bird, that still wouldn't fish him out of this big canyon. My inner voice reminded me—*we're just small fish in a big pond seeking out a smaller fish.* I say "we" knowing that after the first mile and a quarter, most of my party gave up on the search and settling to just watch their steps in challenging terrain.

*Why don't you give up too? You know what you're looking for, but you don't even have a clue of where to begin your search.* My inner monologue was right again. I had a good deal of knowledge, but with non-existent familiarity of the territory, it would take a good deal of searching before I'd be able to dig out hawk.

*All the better*, I answered back.

In this day of GPS and Smart Phones, the human spirit has been deprived of its sense of discovery. A golden age of exploration is lost in the current generation. True, we find our desired destinations and goals with greater ease and efficiency, but the journey has lost its magical appeal. The discovery of what lies between us and our destination has gone the way of the Dodo.

To me, discovery has always had an air of the impromptu about it. The less I know about what I'm stumbling onto, the more accomplished I feel. Funny how that works.

*Too bad it's not working now*, the nagging voice shot across the bow of my mind.

After two hours of hiking, my drive to discover abated. As I dreamed of the air-conditioned car we'd climb into after our adventure, I heard my uncle interject, "Is that your bird?" He pointed at the large, rocking form gliding across the wall of the canyon.

My mind leaped in ecstasy. Effusive emotions poured out my soul. My object had been realized. My mission accomplished.

"Or, is it a Turkey Vulture?" my uncle asked. The sense of satisfaction I attained all too briefly shattered.

To an expert birder, the difference may be apparent. To a neophyte birder of the Southwest, the difference is less visible. This is especially true if you can't see the bold, white bands around the tail and only get a glimpse of your target.

"Uhhh." I stalled for time.

"Well, which is it?" My uncle queried with a touch of impatience. We were all hot and sweaty and grumpy. Having me dither over the identification of this prized possession I'd gone on about probably accentuated the frustration. On the spot as the supposed expert I reluctantly admitted, "I don't know."

"Why not?" The sharp reply.

"Because I've never seen one." The defeated response.

That was it. After a mile and a quarter hike through treacherous terrain, my beautiful, well defined Black-hawk had become just another shadow floating high on the canyon walls. It would have been an easier walk back if we had seen nothing at all.

Even though we observed a number of different birds on the journey back, I wanted that Black-hawk. Each call of the Canyon Wren slapped my ears in defeated desperation. Every shadow of the Yellow-breasted Chat wrenched my eyes from off my feet in hopeful expectation. But my border bird never materialized. The Common Black-hawk would forever be a shadow, floating by my record book.

Upon reaching the steep incline to the parking area, in a burst of energy to seek protection for my deflated self, I charged up toward the vehicles in my shame. I knew the ribbing that would come. All the predicted slams came to pass as, one by one, my exhausted hiking companions gave me a good joshing.

Looking out the window of the car on the way home, my longing for that bird only grew stronger. I wanted that vague silhouette of a bird we saw at the terminus of our expedition to turn into a Black-hawk in the worst way. But putting a check next to the Black-hawk's name on my life list would be a violation of ethics. As my friend told me when I began my birding career: "Birders are disgustingly honest."

I was just disgusted.

"Stop!" I said. "Is that a Raven?"

A dark speck perched fifty feet above us interrupted my pity party. The dark form stood out starkly against the sandy white cliffs. Reaching for my binoculars, I briefly focused on the bird before shouting, "BLACK HAWK! BLACK HAWK!"

We had just hiked nearly two miles to see a bird that we would find as we were leaving the canyon. I was really in for the ribbing now, but I didn't care.

The bird took off as soon as the others had their optics trained on it, giving its fierce, piercing call. His broad, white tail bands shone with an grand luster. He soared right over our car—and into the horizon of discovery.

# The Heaven's Declare

As I wrap up my trip down memory lane highlighting the wonder's seen on my Arizona adventure, it would be unjust to leave out a number of favorite photos. In addition, I include a number of my favorite Psalms of David, all expressing the wonders of God's glorious creations. I hope this trilogy has inspired you to look for God's glory everywhere, even in the driest of deserts. Now, pull up a log around the campfire, and join the "sweet Psalmist of Israel" as he sings of the greatness of God as seen through creation.

*The heavens declare*
*the glory*
*of God.*
*The skies display his*
*craftsmanship.*
*Day after day they*
*continue to speak;*
*night after night, they*
*make him known.*

Psalm 19:1-2 NLT

*They speak without a*
*sound or word; their*
*voice is never heard.*
*Yet their message has*
*gone throughout the*
*earth, and their words to*
*all the world.*

Psalm 19:3-4 NLT

*The Voice of the Lord twists mighty oaks and strips the forests bare.*

*In His temple, everyone shouts "Glory!"*

Psalm 29:9 NLT

*You crown the year with a bountiful harvest; even the hard pathways overflow with abundance.*

Psalm 65:11 NLT

*Those who live at
the ends of the
earth stand in
awe of your
wonders; from
where the sun
rises to where it
sets, you inspire
shouts of Joy!*

Psalm 65:8 NLT

Come mid-July, the Salt Marsh looks more like a nursery than a grassy wilderness . . . You can't swing your binoculars without sighting some small bundle of fuzz . . .

*From Rooted and Restless*

# Rooted and Restless

Half way through the summer season, the young Osprey wait with anxious anticipation for their next meal. Their Father should be by shortly with a nice, juicy fish clutched tightly in his sandpaper-like talons. These hungry, impatient young ones are newborns. The universe has just been introduced to the Ospreys of the future.

To be sure, come mid-July, the Salt Marsh looks more like a nursery than a grassy wilderness. Many of the birds that spend their summers in the marshes along the Atlantic Sea-board are busily tending their brand-new bundles of joy. You can't swing your binoculars without sighting some small bundle of fuzz, eagerly imploring its parents for a meal.

Seeing a beautiful bird like an Osprey attend its offspring is a majestic sight. But if you want a spectacle of spawns, look no further than the Laughing Gull.

Along the East Coast, the Laughing Gull is the common McDonald's parking lot gull of the summer. It's black, gray, and white plumage, along with its bright red bill in breeding season, give the bird a subdued, yet colorful expression. But it's loud, raucous call should alert you to its presence from miles away. And there is no louder time in a Laughing Gull colony then when the young arrive.

In Cape May County, New Jersey, the young arrive in a big way. The largest nesting colony of Laughing Gulls in the world is situated right in the heart of the Salt Marsh. In fact, an estimated one million pairs of Laughing Gulls call the Southern New Jersey marshes their summer home.

When the young arrive, the marshes burst alive with the boisterous calls of proud parents.

Yes, it seems the world is rooted in place for most residents of the marsh. For the moment, most avian families have no intention of taking long trips anytime soon.

But if you look closer, there's restlessness afoot. There—a bird with a destination on his mind has no time to stop and care for a family. There—another bird is on his way to his winter home.

Yes, while most of the local marsh families are settling in to raise their young for the summer, some Shorebirds are already heading south for the winter. These Shorebirds nest high up on the arctic Tundra. Arriving there in late May, they engage in a quick breeding session, and lay their eggs. Most of the eggs hatch in two weeks revealing a tiny fluffball that can already care for itself. Just like a chicken's  chick will peck for food shortly after leaving its egg, these Shorebirds are ready to fend for themselves. This is known as precocial behavior. It leaves the parents free to roam as soon as they've said goodbye to junior, leaving the young to learn migration all by themselves.

It's an odd dynamic out on the marsh in mid-July. Some birds are rooted; some are restless. It's also a perfect example of the Christian's walk—an metaphor with Biblical precedent.

In Colossians 2:7, Paul exhorts a fledgling church with the words, *"So walk in Him, rooted and built up."* It seems an odd request, this command to stand still but keep moving forward, but in the context of the Christian walk, nothing could be more appropriate.

Often, the need to run for God comes upon us, and off we go. Running is fine, as long as we have the firm foundation of the Word of God to lead us onward. Without this basis for our race, we're bound to smash into walls along the way. This is a common fate leaving the Christian bruised, angry, and disillusioned about the life of faith in general.

Oftentimes an opposite situation develops, a scenario in which we become so rooted in our knowledge of God that we forget to run. We've been waiting so long to become secure, we often miss the roads God has built for us to race on.

Yet again, the Bible comes through with balance, and the Great Apostle's solution could not be simpler: Be both. Be rooted and walking. Be firm and fervent to run the race.

Rooted and walking. Yet another wise word from our Father spelled out in His creation all along.

Never have a I sought a reason for personal suffering at a fish cleaning table.

From *Fish and Visitors*

# Fish and Visitors

His rubber-clad hands deftly stripped the juicy meat off the fish.

"Good catch?" I asked, eyeing up his prizes.

"Not bad," he responded. "Caught by a guy this morning. There's about sixteen pounds here in all."

The carcasses piled alongside the cutting table attested to this respectable victory of lure over fish.

When I awoke that morning, I had no idea I would be observing a fish cleaning. No grand visions of flying fish guts filled my mind.

However, I had awoken with a number of trials and tribulations that had been nagging at me for some time. Though these sufferings were nothing in comparison to the horrors in experienced daily by Indian orphans or people in war-torn arenas, pain is pain. Though I feel for the suffering masses worldwide, these personal problems now consumed me and would not be silenced.

I've searched high and low for a cure for suffering. Who hasn't? What logically reasoning soul hasn't sought a deeper explanation for pain experienced the world over—not to mention in their own lives? What thinking human has never stared at the ceiling, wondering why evil and suffering have been allowed to permeate the air we breathe?

I have sought answers and cures and my questions have led me from the psychiatrist's couch to the philosopher's stone.

Never have a I sought a reason for personal suffering at a fish cleaning table.

I watched my friend adroitly cut and lift all the skin from the tender steaks that glistened with moisture beneath. His hands never missed a beat. He held two conversations while still managing to expertly handle his fish.

It slowly dawned on me that one aspect of suffering, at least for a child of God, involves a process with our best interest as the outcome. As we're walking through this life, we step as strangers, pilgrims bound for a better place. But along the way, we tend to accumulate the things of this world. These visitors seem light and airy at first glance, but in the searchlight of Eternity, they prove themselves to be heavy and bulky. Not the sort of freeloaders conducive for a Christian sized journey.

With each quick slice of the fish cleaner's knife, I saw my Heavenly Father stripping away the things that I had accumulated, commenting with each stroke:

"Wood—Gone."

"Hay—Forget it was ever there."

"Stubble—Too worthless for my child."

Even as I write this, the pain of the removal process still grips me. It seems the world does nothing but take, take, take— driving the weary to the point of desperation. When we reach this place of hopelessness in the world, we can almost hear our Father say: *"Give, Give, Give—For there is something that is worth far more than the gold of this world: Your faith."*

"Those are some pretty steaks," I commented, as my friend bagged the remnants of the tuna.

"They sure look a lot better than when they arrived," he commented and walked off.

I looked back into the drum containing the filleted fish.

"One reason for suffering," I said to my captive audience, "is you never know what wisdom will come from the mouth of fishes. I'll bet you know a lot of secrets."

But they're not talking.

# Ode to the Oystercatcher

They're the crowd favorites. The class clowns.

If you ever want to see glazed over eyes turn bright with excitement, all they need to behold is an American Oystercatcher.

What's an Oystercatcher? This beloved bird is a football shaped, mish-mash of colors and features. A common Shorebird of the back bays and salt marshes, this odd-ball is sure to be a show-stopper every time. In fact, his uniqueness has earned him a number of interesting nicknames:

- Bird Wearing a Tuxedo, Smoking a Carrot.
- Keystone Cop of the Bird World.
- Insane Shorebird.
- Bird a Child Would Draw (My favorite appellation)

No matter what sobriquet you apply to the Oystercatcher, this distinctive Shorebird with the bright orange bill gathers attention without fail. But my admiration for the American Oystercatcher lies beyond the superficial and reaches back to a noteworthy quality this bird possesses: its drive to survive.

Today, a survey of an average salt marsh in New Jersey reveals these brightly colored birds in great numbers. However, the experts tell us that nesting in the salt marsh is a new trend for this Shorebird. Years ago, the Oystercatcher primarily nested on the beach.

But no matter how much humans derive enjoyment from miles of sandy beaches, they are no fun for birds nesting on them. The nests of beach birds are under constant attack by crabs, cats, coyotes, crows, and dogs. These enemies of beach nesters find an easy target in a nest positioned in plain sight on a windblown beach.

Some birds, like the Piping Plover, haven't seemed to figure out that the beach is an

67

unsafe area for vulnerable birds. As a result, their population numbers are in a critical state.

But the Oystercatchers have put two and two together, fleeing the beaches and establishing nesting sites in the salt marshes where they are considerably more secure.

Yet another example of the tenacity of this awkward avian is evident in its shifting diet. As the name implies, Oystercatchers love chicken. (Just seeing if you were awake).

Oystercatchers love oysters. In fact, their bills are perfectly designed for cracking open an oyster's shell. Their bills are squished in on the sides, giving them the same design as a shucking knife. With this, they can easily pry open their favored prey.

But in the Delaware Bay region, Oysters went through a serious decline when a blight ran through the population, nearly decimating the Oyster populations of Southern New Jersey.

Would the Oystercatcher disappear along with his favorite food-stuff? Not on your life. Rather than fade away, the Oystercatcher changed his diet. It now feeds on Ribbed-bank Mussels, the common Mollusk of the Salt Marsh.

The Oystercatcher—an impressive bird—has had a myriad of challenges to face, and yet has let nothing stand in its way for survival.

Big, yes. Gawky, yes. Bizarre, yes.

But underneath all the odd features is bird with a will to survive. A bird with reminding us of hope for a world in the throes of change.

# Like a Still Small Voice

Humidity greeted me like a brick wall as I stepped out of my car.

I wasn't expecting it to be this muggy, but I shouldn't have been surprised. Early August in the Mid-Atlantic States generally ushers in the three H's: Hot, Hazy and Humid. This particular day in my favorite marsh of Greenwich, New Jersey, all three unpleasant conditions met together to make a sticky time of year even worse.

But no matter how hot it was, at least there would be activity in the marsh. Or so I thought. It seemed as if all my surroundings were taking siestas, as though the world was on lunch break. I don't blame the world, in this heat.

*There must be some life here*, I thought, looking around in hope for some sign of activity. But all my eyes could make out was the barren marshland surrounding me.

And it was humid.

I suppose there are a number of dynamics to the hobby of birdwatching that keeps thousands of observers coming back for more. Perhaps it's the aesthetic value, the sheer beauty of nature that forces the observer to return time and time again. Or maybe it's the good company that nature lovers attract that turns a hobby into a passion. Maybe the serenity of a walk through the woods is enough to satisfy the longing soul.

One of my favorite aspects of wildlife watching is the fact that you're chasing after life. The nature lover is seeking all the secrets that the world has to offer. The opening of the flowers, the migration of the birds, the fragile life cycle of the butterflies—all these puzzle pieces of life fall into place when you're out watching the natural world unfold.

There are times when the world simply vibrates with the essence of life.

There are other times when it seems like an atom bomb explodes.

*It's humid enough to make you think an atom bomb dropped right here in the marsh,* I moaned to myself, again.

Off in the distance a small flock of migrating Shorebirds cried, giving the coda to their time in North America. They provided a little life with some interest, but too far away to write home about.

As I dragged myself along, the tarmac seemed to move under my feet. I expected a walk without redemption when all of a sudden, a small, flighty object winged its way past my line of sight. *What in the world?*

After circling above me a few times, my winged wonder settled down and revealed itself to be a Red-spotted Purple butterfly. This visual feast sits comfortably on a scale between "beautiful" and "out of this world stunning."

"Thanks for sitting, my beauty," I sweet talked the colorful insect as I drew near. "You stay right there."

A few times the bold butterfly played hard-to-get, took off, and flew around, taunting me the whole time. But with longsuffering and a little perseverance, he finally yielded to the shots I wanted. Click! I recorded some life at last, on a day that lacked anything notable.

This encounter reminded me that no matter how many times you go out in the field looking at the world around you, there will always be a new discovery popping up at an unexpected moment.

The spiritual plain functions in a similar fashion. There are those times, those roads we travel, that seem to have no messages from God whatsoever. We walk on knowing our obedience will be rewarded, but the seeming absence of the Divine increases our longing for more.

The Bible makes the course of action for these moments perfectly clear through its long set of scenarios and precepts: Keep walking. No matter what you feel, no matter what you can see—or not see, no matter what others tell you, don't stray off the path. Keep living as Jesus lived, no matter the situation. Because eventually, His voice rises to your hearing like a still, small whisper.

And sometimes, the whisper has wings.

Although the journey home is difficult and often frightening, He has provided a light for our feet . . .

From *Lost No More*

# The Perfect Storm

When a storm swirled its way up the Bayshore in late summer, we have no choice but to watch. With all haste, we ran to watch the storm roll in. Our hearts out raced our minds as we sped to a wide-open spot we knew well. From there, the storm was center stage. It had no choice but to perform.

*What an odd storm,* you and I thought in unison. And unique. Nothing seemed to fit quite right—a few clouds rolled by, here a lightning strike, there a thunderclap. The usual phenomena of a storm, yes, but thrown together like random ingredients for a untested cake recipe.

We waited for the thunder to follow the lighting. It never came. We anticipated the rain as the sky grew dark. It never materialized. Something was off kilter with this storm, like a meteorological mishap sent as a heavenly jest.

You and I looked deep within each other. We saw the confusion and battered spirits inside our souls. We knew the storm was a reflection of the beauty tossing about within.

Without words we told each other of the fragmented bits of life we felt inside—like ships making contact with solid ground, battered against random rocks along their voyage. It seemed as if our destination was straight ahead, but along the way we ran into a number of twists and turns that knocked us for a loop.

We looked for an anchor within ourselves. There was none. We looked for harbor without. Only found ocean. We sought refuge anywhere we could. No one had answers for our illusions.

We knew faith would have to drive us home. Faith—the inherent knowledge that there is a Grand Artist who can put it all together. Faith—the firm belief that there is a Designer piecing all the disparate elements of our lives together like a celestial quilt woven throughout the heavens.

Realizing it takes a Father of Lights to piece together the scraps of existence we call life was a freeing prospect. No longer wayward souls on a damned voyage; we were heavenly children on a trip home.

Faith cast a whole new light onto the many questions we accumulated along the journey. Suddenly, a storm that made no sense was the perfect storm because there had been a Divine hand behind it all the time.

## Lost No More

Wide grins on the birders' faces coming off the boat told me success was sighted that day.

"Did you see the bird?" I inquired, knowing the answer beforehand.

"Oh yeah!"

"Beautiful bird!"

"The ride is worth the money!"

I'd be riding the boat all right, along with sixteen participants. But today's cruisers were unaware that this tour was a cruise for lost souls.

One day earlier, I had no idea why my boss called, but figured that answering your boss' phone call is a form of job security. "Hi," my boss said, "was there a Brown Booby reported last week?" Brown Booby is a type of seabird normally seen from the waters of Central America and points South.

"There was," I affirmed.

"Well, there's one sitting on a channel marker out in the sound right now!" My excitement could hardly be contained. Even so, the silence I responded with was perfectly natural after such a stunning revelation.

The next day we approached this wayward creature that had set the birding community ablaze. Every form of instant communication among birders filled with messages concerning the whereabouts of this gawky avi-fauna: The Brown Booby.

If the name of this bird sounds a touch silly to you, know that you're in good company. The original discoverers of this species, a group of French Sailors, found the bird doing its mating display. One look at the feet is enough to tell you that this particular dance is rather gawky and uncoordinated. Hence, they gave this weird creature a fitting name. Or, as my boss pointed out, there's a lot of French Sailors having a lot of good laughs every time we find one of these birds.

The bird is a feathered dichotomy: at once gawky and graceful, clumsy and sophisticated. Subtly stunning, yet clearly awkward.

As referenced earlier, the Brown Booby is normally found in the warm waters off Mexico and Puerto Rico. Why we found this one sitting on a channel marker outside of Wildwood, New Jersey, is anyone's guess. Some suggested that a strong, southerly wind pushed the bird towards the Garden State. Others thought it might have been an odd dispersal, as other sightings of this species have been noted along the Eastern Seaboard.

No matter how it got here, it was lost. But not alone. Since it had been found three days earlier, the birding community rallied to fervently seek views of the vagrant. The longest a Booby has stuck around is a day and a half in our area, and often proved uncooperative for birding bliss. This one, however, seemed to have tape on its feet, acting as a perfect specimen for lengthy looks. The bird was lost, but it could never be described as isolated. It had too many people looking for it.

Similar to the child of God. With all the happenings in the world, it's easy to slip into despair and feel lost. At times, it seems currents of regret and doubt sweep us away into the dark caverns of our minds.

At times, it feels as if all is lost. But we have a message from the Father who is stronger than our feelings:

- The message tells us that although the difficulties of life may cause us to question our sonship, He has us carved into His hands.

- The message tells us that although the journey home is difficult and often frightening, He has provided a light for our feet.

- The message tells us He came to seek and save the lost. A promise we can take to the bank the next time loneliness and despair creep in. God's out there looking for us, waiting to run to us with open arms.

Arms that are ready to shepherd the lost safely home.

# In the Shade of the Mimosa Tree

I wasn't really sitting in the shade of the Mimosas that humid August afternoon, but the title sounds like it should be a Eugene O'Neill play. It's been rattling around my head for the past several weeks.

Here, I open a doorway for you to view my special place—a place of refuge closed to the rest of humanity. I'm not the only one with this type of hide-away. Most, if not all, people have a place the retreat to for safe observation and contemplation. The idea even has biblical precedent in the concept of a prayer closet.

So, let's take a walk through my secluded spot and hopefully you'll be inspired to leave no corner unexplored in your secret space.

Stepping from my car, my ears are suddenly assaulted by the electric tones of an Eastern Kingbird. This bird may be small, but it seems to be infected with Napoleon's Disease (small, but big chip on its shoulder). His scientific name is Tyrannus tyrannus which, means tyrant of tyrants, and I'm sure the number of birds that he has harassed could attest to this designation.

From the small and bossy, to the small and gentle, this Common Buckeye sat waiting for the sun to peek over the cloud, giving him a bit of an energy boost. Butterflies need their internal body temperatures at around eighty degrees in order to maintain optimum flight. This poor fellow has a bit of his wing missing. Maybe he met the Kingbird.

This rusty-colored Dragonfly is probably a Needham's Skimmer. Dragonflies are cool. At once aloof and alert, they roam the air with an intensity hard to imagine. Dragonflies are also our good friends since they eat a lot of mosquitoes.

I'm always surprised at how quickly the trees betray fall's arrival. It seems earlier every year, or perhaps it's my memory playing tricks on me. Here's a Sassafras Tree showing the struggle between Autumn and summer. Life and death. You can make Sassafras Tea and Root Beer from the roots of this gorgeous plant.

Let's take a pause and enjoy the Eastern Comma in repose. He may be practicing for the long overwintering stage that comes for him later on. Upon finding a hollow tree or clump of leaf litter, these beautiful bugs will spend the colder months in our area.

Back to our birds. This Mockingbird demonstrated his heartiness by continuing to sing well into the afternoon, past the time when birds need to sing. Mockingbirds are our most talented mimics and are adept at imitating other species of birds. But birds are not the only things subject to this mimicry. Mockingbirds can mimic anything from car alarms to police sirens, too.

And finally, though I didn't take refuge under the shade of the Mimosa, others utilized this colorful non-native plant. This Spicebush Swallowtail has found some intriguing nectar in the pink flowers of the Mimosa. It doesn't belong in our area, but it is beautiful, and wildlife has adapted to its presence.

Finally, here's hoping you get a chance to sail away on the tides of discovery. And discovery starts right in your own back yard.

Let's take a walk through my secluded spot and hopefully you'll be inspired to leave no corner unexplored in your secret space.

From *In the Shade of the Mimosa Tree*

September 11, 2011

# In the Form of a Dove

Whenever a rare bird shows up around Cape May, it can expect its privacy to be invaded within minutes of its discovery. Like a well-oiled machine, instant communication devices alert birders of avian anomalies with unimaginable speed.

I am often the benefactor of these high-tech reports, and when I heard of a Eurasian Collared-Dove nearby, I wasted no time. I jumped in my car and followed the precise directions to the location of interest.

On the way, I formulated a mental picture of the bird so I could have a head start on finding it. I imagined myself standing there, like a ninny, in front of the neighborhood homes of Cape May Point, helplessly scanning the telephone wires. You never know how rare birds will act. They're rare, they have free reign to act however they feel fit.

I slowly coasted up to the address where the sighting was pinpointed and saw my feathered prize.

Quietly, I got out of my car. In synchronization with my body leaving the driver's seat, the bird nonchalantly flew up on a wire, staring at me as if I had been late for some long-standing appointment.

You never know how rare birds will act, I sardonically noted.

But before I could finish my thought, the unexpected happened. My car door slipped from my grip causing a loud bang to echo through the vinyl canyons of Cape May Point. "Ugh," I grunted, shamed at my lack of discipline and expecting the worst. But it was no matter to my feathered friend. He simply stretched his neck and preened a few feathers. "That didn't startle you, did it?" If doves understand rhetorical questions, I imagine he found it very profound.

If my lack of vigilance didn't scare this bird from his roost, the BMW suddenly roaring down the street surely would. I leaped behind my car to avoid becoming a fatality on the grill

81

of such a nice vehicle. The driver continued to talk on his phone, completely unaware that he was doing well above the speed limit.

Once past, I rose from behind my shelter only to be serenely greeted by my European visitor yet again.

"You're made of sterner stuff than I, my friend." If doves understand compliments, I'm sure his ego must have swelled a little.

After a few more moments of observation, I got in my car and left the Arnold Schwarzenegger of doves behind. As I drove off along the tourist-stocked streets, I thought of the importance of doves in biblical literature. They acted as assurances of dry land after floods gone by. They were an integral element of the romance between King Solomon and his beloved. They picture innocence to our Lord.

But perhaps most importantly, we're told that at the beginning of Christ's ministry the Holy Spirit was sent to Him "like a dove." This picture of the peaceful power of the Holy Ghost has been a familiar visual to the saved and unsaved alike. Whether it's used as an emblem for the Quakers or Calvary Chapel churches, the impact the picture of the dove has had on Christianity is profound.

I need that Dove in my life. I need the Holy Spirit more than bread. More than water. A life invaded by the Holy Spirit is just like that dove sitting unconcerned on the wire. No matter how many door slams life throws at me, I can sit in perfect peace, too.

I find encounters with the Holy Ghost predictable: He's available to meet with me whenever I choose to seek him. In the same way I felt the dove greeted me like a long-lost friend, a search for the Holy Helper is always fruitful. I couldn't imagine winning battles without this Crucial Comforter. Through His help the Word of God leaps off the page and cuts straight through my heart. It's His coming along side that takes the fleshly tendencies in me, once so dominant, and keeps them far away from my mind. It's His gentle leading that shepherds me in this earthly pilgrimage.

I remember once chatting with a friend when a white dove flew by. It was probably released from a nearby wedding. This prompted some long-lost religious memory in my friend as he quickly asked, "What's the point of the Holy Spirit? From all I remember, all he did was put tongues of fire on people's heads."

I shrugged my shoulders, knowing a sufficient explanation would be lost on my friend. That knowledge can only be attained empirically. That information can only be known by those who have had an experience with God's Comforter.

# Perpetually Perfect

I have spent a good deal of time around artists in the few years I've walked this earth. And whenever I come away from an experience with an artist, I feel a sense of awe. Whether they are a photographer, painter, or poet, they all generally possess a skill most of us long for—the ability to capture a perfect moment in time.

The artwork these talents leave behind are monuments to the moments in time we cherish, rare spaces in life where everything seems to fit just right. Those who capture these rare, harmonious happenings are the artists whose influence stands the longest. Here are three of my favorite pieces of art.

This pull-along, male Wood Duck was my first toy. Ever. It was hand-made by a neighbor, a kindly woman who eventually succumbed to breast cancer. As it stands, this duck holds a lot of significance in my life. It serves as a reminder of the giving soul who took so much time and energy to produce a well-crafted toy for a newborn down the street.

It also serves as a reminder of the beauty that surrounds us in the natural world. I forgot I still had this toy when I started exploring wildlife. Before I rediscovered it, the Wood Duck had become my favorite waterfowl. When I look on this simple pull-along toy, I am reminded of the many times I've encountered this bird in nature, serenely floating along some wooded pond. Such sudden instances of peace and calm keep me grounded as life goes by at a frantic pace.

Twenty-two years later, I received this intricate carving of an American Avocet for a birthday present, a piece of art demanding attention. I remember showing this gift to one of the world's finest birders soon after receiving it. His strong show of approval over the carver's merit were well founded.

But even more impressive than the carving would have to be the paint job. Every fine plumage detail is captured in all its glory here. I have seen countless other carvings of the same bird, and none come close to this fine piece of workmanship.

My most recent acquisition is this depiction of a Blackburnian Warbler painted by a friend from my church, Noah Brown. Titled "Alert," it shows a fine spring-plumage "fire-throat" on the outlook for potential danger. When I received this painting a few weeks ago, I stood a bit paralyzed by the attention to detail expended upon my commission. The depth of field, the stark colors, the single dead leaf, all these intricacies added up to a phenomenal purchase. I had always complimented my friend on her distinctive artwork. With this picture, she raised the bar significantly.

With all these perpetually perfect moments stored in my mind, I find a quiet place and take a walk with a Friend. Not just any Friend, but the Name above all Names, the Friend above all Friends. In some cool, verdant region, I stroll along with the Creator in a perfect abode. It's an area where the squeals of Wood Ducks ring like pleasant melodies in their Maker's ears. A region where American Avocets fly by with all the freedom they were intended to have. A special place where Blackburnian Warblers no longer sing for the sake of survival, but for the sake of His glory.

We walk along, talking about the topics that are near and dear to our hearts. In the cool of the evening, we find communion as natural as if we were never separated. Somewhere along our stroll, I look to His face, and ask Him the question that sits somewhere within each believer, "How can I walk with you?"

"Because I love you," comes the concise reply.

"But I swear—by accident. Now and then," I confess involuntarily.

"I know," the cool, unaffected response returns.

"Don't you know how prideful I can act?" I question, hoping to see some sign of pity. Instead, I only find His knowing look.

"I know you were prideful a few days ago. I know you will be so tomorrow, too," comes the unexpected response.

"Then how can I walk with you?" I ask again, with undertones of bewilderment.

"Because you're perpetually perfect, my friend." The response cuts through my tired questions, bringing balm to my tired spirit. He continues, "Because of the love and dedication of My Son, you are washed and holy in My sight. I see you through the Blood of my Son. I have captured you as you were always meant to be."

I pause, reeling in the truth of who I am. I have been captured perpetually perfect. I have good standing with my Friend of Friends, Lord of Lords. We exchange glances. Mine express overwhelmed emotions. His express His faithfulness and grace. We continue on, confident that this is a walk that will never end.

Somewhere, I suspect that there are beauty pageants for birds.

From *Apples of His Eyes*

# Apples of His Eyes

Somewhere, I suspect that there are beauty pageants for birds. Here's my imagination at work, my educated guess at what these displays of avi-fauna attractiveness look like.

Our first contestant is the ever popular, ever loved, Eastern Bluebird! Their nickname is the "Bird with Earth on its breast, and Sky on its back." And what a beauty they are!

But these neat little thrushes are more than pretty face. They advocate for those in need of housing. Hundreds and hundreds of bluebird houses are erected every spring for these fantastic fliers to seek shelter in.

This species is also the poster child for magazine covers, coffee table books, and sweaters that somehow find their way into thrift stores time and time again. They're industrious, crafty, and full of vim and vinegar. Who couldn't fall in love with that vibrant mix of electric blue and rusty brown?

Yes, it's everyone's favorite: the fun, the flashy, the endearing Eastern Bluebird!

*(Thunderous Applause; Whistles, Cheers)*

Next in line is . . . is . . . is . . . well . . . the Chipping Sparrow. It measures five and a half inches long, is gray and brown. Its song sounds like an insect.

*(Polite Applause. Then silence. Then crickets.)*

So, there we have it; America's darling of a songbird, the Eastern Bluebird.

*(The Crowd Goes Wild!)*

And that sparrow you sometimes see in your backyard that needs a voice lesson.

(The Crowd Sits Down.)

Okay, cast your votes. But while you're doing that, this word just came in from our sponsor:

The Chipping Sparrrow, though small and dull, has God's presence promised it. Guaranteed. A Chippy can't die without God being there. No matter how dull and gray they may be . . . His eyes are on the sparrow.

*(The Crowd Leans Forward, Longing. They Want to Be a Sparrow)*

Just a needed reminder that God's presence can turn any popularity contest on its head.

# Breath of God

For seven months of the year, we tend to take trees for granted. Particularly in Southern New Jersey, the notion of driving by hundreds of these majestic creations is something taken as matter of fact.

But come October, the trees announce their presence in earnest. They herald their existence in exclamations too loud to miss. Like tragic heroes about to die, they make their presence known in a most dramatic fashion.

Lining the roadsides of many local towns grow Sassafras trees in large numbers. They exhibit a wide variety of colors come the fall. These trees paint with a palette encompassing anything from light green to deep red.

Unlike the other wildlife I like to observe, trees sit still long enough to let me make my judgments about their aesthetic appeal. At times, they seem straight and narrow, as plain as any other tree. Viewed from underneath, the leaves transform into a dazzling kaleidoscope of bewildering reds and greens.

This Black Gum shows the typical fall foliage of the species sporting many various shades of red, usually leaning toward the darker shade of the spectrum.

Note the close-up view of Black Gum leaves:

But these creatures of beauty are not just pretty faces. This Winged Sumac Shrub provides valuable seeds for migrating songbirds. This particular shrub shows the grapple between life and death, summer and autumn.

Trees are valuable to God as well. The Lord references them numerous times in the writing of His Word. Whether it's comparing the strength of a nation to the Cedars of Lebanon or comparing the strength of the godly to a tree planted by a river, it's hard to get away from these wondrous creations in God's testament.

We should be thankful for Autumn. It allows for a time when God lets his less appreciated creation strut their stuff. We also need the reminder about how crucial these trees are to our wellbeing. Trees absorb sunlight in large amounts, letting us enjoy their shade. They give us the wood with which we shelter just about everything we hold dear and produce the oxygen necessary for survival, giving off the breath of God.

These few reasons barely scratch the surface of the benefits given to mankind by these sleeping giants. We have much to praise God for in the gift of these woody beauties. And if the awe and wonder of a sassafras tree gone up in metaphorical flames were the only reason to give thanks, that would be reason enough.

**Andrew Hughes** ▶ **David Lord**

Thursday at 10:26 AM · 👥

"And if the awe and wonder of a sassafras tree...were the only reason to give thanks, that would be reason enough." Photo and quote by David Lord.

*Pastor Andrew Hughes*

# Veteran's Day

*Note: I wrote this piece some years ago about an experience at a Veteran's Museum that shook me visibly with great impact. No veteran should ever be forgotten. That is a lofty exhortation, but if we try to make it happen, we will honor our ignored heroes greatly.*

The warm Texas sun glistened off the beautiful statue. I had never seen anything like it. It was mammoth, made out of bronze, I believe, and fitting in its simplicity. The soldiers raising the flag at Iwo Jima is a powerful sight in a photographic image, but to see it so huge before me was a truly fitting tribute to those marines who gave everything they had so that we could have everything we want.

Sound trite? These statements get bandied about a good deal, but they carry extreme importance. It's close to impossible to justly capture what these people gave in service of their country.

We were in South Texas on that warm March day. Our vacation was coming to a close, and we could definitely call this trip a success. The birding had been good, the people friendly, and the scenery gorgeous.

But we had some time to kill before our plane took off, so my Dad pulled this destination out of the thin blue air. I have no idea how he found this place in a state we had never been in before—but find it we did. It was a memorial to the Marines who served in the Pacific, with a special emphasis on Iwo Jima.

The special emphasis came in the form of a huge gold statue in the middle of a field. It was awe inspiring, and I wish I could remember more. I have photos, but they don't seem to do justice to this triumph of sculpture. There was a lot of information about the sculptor, but I can't recall any of it.

But I do recall the gift shop. There were mugs, DVDs, mousepads, T-Shirts, you name it, it was probably in there. It also doubled as a museum where a large number of school-children were taking a tour. The noise grated on my nerves so I moved to a corner where a large number of sweatshirts and hats would muffle the cacophony of giggles and screams.

In the corner of this room was a standard fold up chair. I glanced behind me and saw a WWII era veteran of the USMC working his careful way to the chair.

Then I broke down.

I had wanted to go up and laud him for his wonderful service to his country. I wanted to tell him all the wonderful things I had experienced because he believed that the "Nazi master race" needed to go no further. His actions allowed me to grow up in a Christian home, not worrying if I was not living up to a standard. Without him, and others like him, I would not be able to see the fifty-two birds I had seen on this trip.

But I broke down.

Just to see his frail old frame sitting there, lonely, desolate, forgotten by most of the people he had worked to keep free, stirred something unmentionable in me. It grabbed my soul and tore down my defenses.

I had grand things to say to him, but I couldn't bring myself to say them. I shook his hand, stared him directly in the eye, and thanked him. He may not have heard, because my voice was cracking with emotion. Then I went into the map room and felt the storm of emotions well up inside.

I spent the plane ride home reading, categorizing my life birds, and thinking. Had I said enough to that Marine veteran? Did I say too much? Did he think me crazy for the visible discomfort on my face as we talked? I don't know because my emotions got the better of me at the time.

Now six or seven months have gone by. Birds have migrated through, graduation has come and gone, girlfriends have come and gone, work, play, college, all these things have had their season in my life and have passed. But I silently hope that honored old man still sits in that museum and gift shop. I hope he sits there as an immutable reminder to us all, of the courage and sacrifice of all veterans.

Thank a Veteran any day you have the chance.

Thank God for what He's given us through them.

# One Wing Heaven, One Wing Earth

I stand facing the seemingly endless expanse of stage in front of me. I am a simple spectator, wrought with tense expectation. The show promises to be a good one. I should know. I've seen it here before.

My anticipation fluctuates with every breath of air that brushes the tawny reeds. I stand still, breathlessly expecting the grand overture to begin. My mind wanders. The next moment I'm in la-la land thinking about everything but the spectacle I came to be privy to.

The wait is forever. Not that it seems like forever. It is forever. I pace the empty auditorium only to find it less vacant than I originally suspected. There's a bluebird sending his constant "cheer-up" message my way. "No, I don't have to cheer up!" I shout. "Get off my shoulder, old man!"

That'll show him.

From the west wing comes a big flock of Meadowlarks, golden drops of technicolor sunshine just waiting for Judy Garland to start singing *Over the Rainbow*. But even these bright, cheery creatures are no consolation for the absence of the transcendent.

The transcendent.

It keeps me going. It reminds me every time I walk outside that I am engaging a natural world that showcases the collision of the physical and the spiritual.

There is something beyond this world. I feel it in my bones every time I lift my binoculars heavenward to look at a bird in flight. Every time I watch a butterfly wing past, stopping to nectar. Every time I hear the songs of Warblers, singing in the distance of my memory. These are the moments I know that I know that we are not alone.

*"RRRRR"* That strangely familiar trill ripples down my spine, ripping me from my thoughts.

There are the players this expectant spectator has longed to see. Flying high above the marsh are sixteen large gray birds. Their wing beat so dreamlike, Debussy would turn green with envy. Their call so ancient, so mysterious, it would awaken atavistic longings in the most modern soul.

They are Sandhill Cranes. Just sixteen birds, a mere pittance compared to the 500,000 that invade Nebraska every spring. But still, they are sufficient to send my imagination whirling into the distant past. One bird alone could send a spirit soaring.

Photo by Jeff White

I watch the majestic forms fly over my head. Their calls I hear more with my heart than with my ears. I watch as they sail out of sight, leaving me longing for one more look.

"There must be more than this . . ." I mutter. The last glimpse of their imperial form confirms this notion.

I leave the theater, amazed, entranced, and wanting more.

"Cheer-up" intones the bluebird on my way out.

"All right" I concede. "Have it your way."

# An Interview with Mr. D.

A heavenly aura filled the room, ebbing and flowing like some half-forgotten body of water in man's memory. The lights were very bright, but this did not seem to bother the girl at the desk. No, it appeared as if nothing would perturb her. In fact, a fall from Grace could take place right before her eyes and still not one stroke of her filing would be amiss. She sat there, cool and tranquil, chewing her gum.

I, on the other hand, sat sweaty palm in sweaty palm, staring at the ground. Too scared to move, too scared to speak. "Excuse me, Gloria?" I said, summoning all the courage I could muster. "Could you hurry him up? I've got things to do, and I'm not used to the time zone shift yet. Jet lag is still hanging on."

The secretary looked up at me with the speed of a cow during milking, and said in a most unearthly nasal voice, "Why don't you start walking, by the time you get there, he should be ready." I agreed. "When he's ready for you, his door will turn from red to green."

"Like the signs on an airplane bathroom," I offered to lighten the mood. The only light I saw at present were lightning flashes and low rumbles of thunder. My nervous chuckles responded to her demeaning chuckles behind the receptionist's desk.

To interrupt the awkward moment, two enormous gates opened their masses toward us, revealing a grand stairway. "Is this the . . . uh . . ." I inquired, not being able to say Stairway to Heaven. Two apathetic nods were the only reply I received.

I started up the steps, and simultaneously began to think. Judging by the size of the stairway, I had plenty of time to think.

How would I approach him? Cordially of course, but with determination. I had to be completely frank in all my motions. Surely, he would respond to this. After all, he was the greatest character builder in the 19th century. Perhaps in all of history. If I was honest and frank and to the point, this would certainly gain me a more favorable reception.

To be sure, honesty must be a big part of my success. He knew the difference between a truth and a lie. As simple as that may seem, he has it down to an art. There would be no buffaloing this guy.

Number one on my list of things to avoid: Autographs! This would screw up everything royally. It would show me in an insincere light, which would ruin the whole interview. This mission is too important for that. No autographs. Ever.

"Man, this is taking an eternity!" I bemoaned. At that instant, the stair moved. "Thanks," I offered the entity in charge of the stairs. I wonder what Led Zeppelin would think of an escalator in heaven.

The doors to his office were huge. I stood in amazement and awe at the beautiful engravings. Soon, I was to enter these doors. Was I prepared? What if I goofed up? Would I get a second chance?

My thoughts were interrupted by the silent creaking of the doors gliding effortlessly apart, revealing something beyond all imagination. The room was an exact replica of his office on earth, only ten times grander than anything earth could ever offer. I stood in awe of its beauty, in spite of the fact that my visibility was limited.

Even though it was hard to perceive, I saw a figure at the desk. Before I knew it, I was greeted by a hand. Not a particularly welcoming hand, but one that assured me I would be honored here.

"I thank you for receiving me sir, you're very kind." I criticized every word I said, just waiting to mess up.

"What can I do for you?" A kind, yet firm voice intoned.

*Do for me? Do for me? What haven't you done for me, Mr. Dickens! Here I am, here civilization is, 200 years after your first earthly cry, and we are not same. We are moved by your characters and the figments of your imagination that have taken the world by storm. Do for me? Why, I would have never survived those boring, monotonous hours between college classes without David Copperfield. Without Bleak House. How different those twilight hours in the late summer would have seemed. Why, in fact, Great Expectations and A Tale of Two Cities are perhaps the two greatest examples of sacrifice next to the Gospels themselves. You, Mr. Dickens, have done so much for us, a universe without you scarcely bears thinking about.*

But these thoughts never materialized in the factory between my brain and my mouth. They just sat there in backstock. Waiting. He looked at me with a silent tolerance, waiting for me to speak.

"Can I have your autograph? Sir?" I whined for lack of words.

More silence.

Happy 200th Birthday, Mr. Dickens! May your works live on well past 200 years.

# Day of Discovery

Our dog is a faithful dog.

She began as a seeing eye project who just missed muster on her exams. Putting this failure behind her, she came to live with us. Needless to say, the seeing eye's loss is our gain.

For over a decade, our gentle, lovable Golden Retriever, Halo, has graced our company with her playful, if absent-minded, hijinks. We laugh at her eagerness to chase her tail. We smile at her willingness to please. We smirk at her half-hearted attempts to chase the ubiquitous deer off our property.

But what I appreciate most about our Halo is her sense of discovery. This commitment to exploration of the surrounding world is not unique to her. Every dog worth its salt should share an ever-curious nose. Watching my dog sniff out new areas with all the eagerness and wide-eyed wonder of Marco Polo is truly special. So, I try to maximize her exposure to unknown regions to explore. She is just as eager to explore as anyone has ever been.

I took her to Turkey Point recently, a secluded, natural area on the banks of the Delaware Bayshore. Its wonder has never failed to capture my imagination. I was curious to see how Halo would respond to the new surroundings. First on discovery's unlimited menu: Moss. Sphagnum Moss is a dense carpet of vibrant color in an otherwise gray winter landscape. Also known as Peat Moss, this non-vascular organism has served mankind in a variety of uses over time, including use as fertilizer or even a diaper for Native American children.

Moving on. Halo's found a Fern. Many types of Ferns decorate our local woodlands. Whether Cinnamon or Fiddle-head, these fascinating plants serve as a beautiful under-story accent. Ferns thrive in moist climates, which explains why in the forests of Britain, I found Ferns the size of my head, (bigger than you think). But anyway, good job Halo. Your nose has not let you down so far. See if it can find you something in the animal kingdom.

Ah, my canid friend has found the remnants from another canid friend, probably a Coyote. This wily creature has made his abode in a berm surrounding a nearby pond. Halo knows that this is the most interesting find so far. In this very hole, one of her distant relatives has set up shop, and done quite well, if the demise of the deer population is any sign.

It's wonderful to watch new horizons of knowledge open up for people—and dogs. It must be such a joy to be an educator, to sense the smiles form on virgin minds when a new concept is grasped. I see it all the time when I educate others on nature, and it has built the most rewarding type of job imaginable—sharing knowledge with others. It brings to mind the quote which has become a maxim:

*"If you have knowledge, let others light their candles by it."*

Not only a maxim, a God-given purpose to define our lives by.

But perhaps the most important discovery of all came toward the end of our walk. Discoveries are endless as we found on the brisk February afternoon when we walked through the woodlands of Turkey Point. Up ahead was only one trail left to explore. Halo fearlessly led the charge when the woods suddenly opened up to a picturesque vista overlooking the marshes of the Delaware Bayshore. We looked on as Black Ducks winged by in their usual brisk hurry. We watched the Great Blue Heron abscond with a cacophony of grunts and squawks accompanying. But mostly, we watched the horizon, knowing the horizon of discovery to be loaded with possibilities.

Onward, Halo. The discoveries of God's creation are endless. And we don't want to miss a single one.

Here's hoping you get a chance to sail away on the tides of discovery. And discovery starts right in your own backyard.

From *In the Shade of the Mimosa Tre*

101

when the view is from this point of reference,
we would be most impolite to refuse.

# European Travel Journal
## Introduction by Jon-Mark Grussenmeyer

David Lord was many things to me—a treasured friend, a fellow actor, a birdwatching tutor, and a theatre-going companion. But some of my most cherished memories of David come from our time travelling together in Europe.

I have spent many years studying medieval history while living in the beautiful old city of Canterbury, and in that time, I have given countless tours of the city and its magnificent cathedral to an assortment of family and friends. Most people appreciate the sights; some even seem to enjoy my accompanying barrage of historical details.

But few have truly *seen* Canterbury the way that David did when he first came to stay with me after I had first moved to the UK in 2011. In fact, I am not sure that 'sightseeing' is a word that can adequately describe his way of experiencing the places that we went—one glance at his blog posts 'Hallowed Halls' and 'Keeper of the Castle' makes that obvious.

David *felt* Canterbury Cathedral and its rich past steeped in constant Christian worship stretching back more than 1,500 years. His way of processing such things, both in the moment and later when he returned home and wrote his blog posts, made a lasting impression on me and deepened my own appreciation for my beloved cathedral city.

David did not only feel deeply and see evidence of God in cathedrals, however. When we visited castles, which merely elicited technical observations about military architecture from me, he saw poignant allegories of God's power and love. David's blog invokes the Psalms often, which was, I think, eminently fitting for a man who, like his biblical namesake, saw the hand of God in every little detail of natural beauty or man-made splendor. In contrast, I realized that I was looking only with academic eyes, and it humbled me.

Touring was always secondary to David when we travelled together. He said to me many times that what he really wanted was to 'live like a local' for a little, to truly come to understand another culture. We thus spent many an hour in village pubs, sampling the ale while he charmed the locals with his genuine interest in all things English.

I regret to say that I felt compelled to dampen slightly that sense of interest on occasion;

while walking through my village one morning, for instance, he noticed a bird that caused him to shout, "A Great Tit! A Great Tit!" echoingly down the street until I convinced him to lower his voice.

David carried the same sense of enthusiasm and wonder when we travelled together to northern France to see my brother, Timothy, who was then teaching English abroad. In Paris, he marveled at Notre Dame and the Eiffel Tower, but he equally relished his first authentic Belgian waffle in Brussels, as his subsequent blog post attests.

At some point, Timothy and I informed David of some of the cultural differences between France and New Jersey, including the fact that one should always give a greeting when entering a shop and politely thank the shopkeeper and say goodbye on the way out; in fact and very unlike New Jersey, often people will amicably say hello simply when passing on the street. David immediately took this to heart and began to shout, 'Bonjour!!', at random passers-by with such intense exuberance that I am certain several old Frenchmen nearly suffered minor heart attacks. No one could ever claim that he refused to enter into the culture of places that he visited with all his heart and soul.

I was once again living in Canterbury when I heard the news of David's passing. For the most part, I simply felt helpless and isolated, unable to be with his family and all who held him dear to give and seek comfort as we struggled to come to grips with such an enormous loss.

However, being in England was also oddly consoling in a way as I remembered afresh the profound manner in which David had experienced the rolling countryside and towering cathedral. In the days that followed, I found myself walking the ways that we had walked together three years before, and I went to evensong, with the words of his 'Hallowed Halls' drifting through my mind.

I did not simply see or hear that night in Canterbury Cathedral—I *felt* the meaning of those beautifully sung prayers and the presence of God in those ancient stone walls. It struck me suddenly that it was the Feast of All Saints, and I wept then in the middle of the service—in grief for David's loss to us left on earth, in thanks that he numbered among the saints, and in utter gratitude that God had blessed me with such a friend.

For me, David will never truly be gone; he lives on in the very way that I view my English home, and every time I walk through the peaceful aisles of the cathedral, I think of him as one of the 'distinguished shadows' who graced that sacred space. And I smile, knowing that, one day, that intrepid traveler will greet me once again with a vigorous, 'Bonjour!'

And every time I walk through the peaceful aisles of the cathedral, I think of him as one of the 'distinguished shadows' who graced that sacred space.

*Jon-Mark Grussenmeyer*
February 6, 2012

# Hallowed Halls

The chill of a Canterbury Evening is a chill like no other. It really blows my mind, but this is the same chill Thomas Becket must have felt in December 1170, before he met some knights with a different sense of reverence than he had.

"I'm late for Evensong," I mutter, mad at myself that I can't find the entrance. Didn't the people in the twelfth century have any idea of signage? A simple "Ye Are Getting Hotter," would have been sufficient. But no. I'm left to wander among the cloisters on a moonlit Canterbury evening sans guidance.

I finally find my way into the Cathedral. Once there, I'm pleasantly greeted and directed by an usher to the place where evensong will be conducted.

Inside, I take my seat along with all the other participants. We sit simply and contentedly, listening to the bells ring. I don't know how old the bells are, but with each gong, I feel as if their triumphant heralds have echoed through the hollows of time.

The bells fall silent. Conversations die away among the whispers in the cathedral and the boys' choir enters.

In the states, I've heard the Philadelphia's Boys Choir, and they are very good. But the ancient tradition that these boys take part in adds a deep, meditative quality to their high-pitched strains. I wonder if these boys appreciate the sacred ritual they're allowed to participate in.

All eyes focus on the choir as they begin to sing. With Psalm book in hand, I think back to the young Israeli King who originally penned these words. I wonder if his spirit is with us now, approving of how his words have survived the ages, to once again be sung by those expressing their love to God.

It was Thanksgiving back in the United States, so a strange irony struck me when the minister approached the pulpit and read from Revelation 16. In this passage, 100-pound hailstones fall on people. I imagined the joyful hymns and Psalms of praise back home contrasting with this bleak prophecy and suppressed a sick snicker.

The service broke.

The seats vacated.

The boys choir made their way to the vestry once again. Another day's work done.

But I stayed behind to ponder a little, thinking about all the Kings, Queens, and other various rulers who have graced this marvelous hall.

How many souls of historical import have mingled within these beautiful stones? How lucky I am to be adding my footprints to such a distinguished list of shadows.

Once outside, the wind grows bitterer still, and my coat proves too thin for the brisk, English air. But as I walk away, I witness the moon rise over that mammoth cathedral structure. And the memories of young voices mingling with ancient stone is enough to get me home warm enough.

March 3, 2012

## Keeper of the Castle

Leeds Castle.

A beautiful, historic structure jutting straight up from the English countryside, reminding the traveler of a time when castles were an everyday sight.

This beautiful castle constructed nearly 900 years ago, has witnessed many historical figures waltzing their way through these grounds. The most famous would have to be a certain grotesquely obese monarch and his unfortunate harem.

That's right, King Henry the 8th—the king everyone loves to hate—claimed this delightful 500-acre site as the perfect summer home and converted it to such in honor of his first wife, Catherine of Aragon.

As a child, whose youthful imagination was stoked by the coals of such masterpieces as *The Chronicles of Narnia*

and the King Arthur fables,

Leeds was a perfect castle.

This section of the castle, a more recent addition, served to conjure up images of Knights and Maidens riding steeds out of the mists of Albion (the ancient Roman word for Britain).

Everything I'd read about was so real before me. Pictures engraved themselves upon my memory as with a searing iron.

I've been in Europe before, but these images stick out among the rest as what the Medieval world should be.

Looking at the castle, I couldn't help but remember the wonderful songs the sweet Psalmist of Israel wrote long before Leeds was even an idea in some architect's mind:

*Lift up your heads, O gates,*
*And be lifted up, O ancient doors,*
*That the King of Glory may come in!*
Psalm 24:7 NIV

And no matter how glorious Henry thought he was, (or at least his grocer thought he was), it's comforting to think that there is a King whose glory lasts forever.

110

Inside the castle, actual round head armor from the 17th century greeted us! It fascinated me to think that this armor was probably used in the English Civil War. Makes me want to go pummel some Puritans.

Another fascinating relic was this bathtub that Catherine of Aragon used. In keeping with the modest culture of the day, she would bathe with her robe on. How you get clean when covered with a robe is beyond me, but more power to her.

History is a wonderful thing. It grows even more vibrant when you experience the ruins of time for yourself. Setting my watch back a millennium or so I've stood in the Colosseum where I could hear crowds roar and the clash of the gladiators' swords as they fought in their merciless fights.

I've stood in Ephesus, in front of that great library of the ancient world and listened for the echoes of an excited church reading a letter from their spiritual mentor.

I've walked the streets of Tombstone and have felt the bullets whiz by as two factions finally sought to rectify their differences.

But Leeds was different. In Leeds, I became a part of the history. I was a servant preparing the inordinate amount of food to feed a gross caricature of a monarch. I was the priest reciting mass in the chapel. I was among the congregation releasing guilt.

Leeds was history flowing through my veins. I immersed myself in a sweet, misty dream.

All dreams end. As we made our way further into the castle, a distinct change washed over the structure. Suddenly, gaudy paintings of black swans lined the halls. The color of the rooms switched from subtle stone to loud pastel.

We were in the 1930s. In the early part of the Twentieth century, a socialite bought the castle, and preserved half of it in its original state, while the other half turned into her personal playground.

My attention span turned off at this point. As much as early British history fascinates me and I find it tasteful (my subjective view), the early 20th Century was gaudy and frivolous (also my subjective opinion). But, I did admire her book collection.

History is nothing but change. Watching the transition from early 15th century to early 20th at Leeds drove this point home in a vivid manner. With so many changes in the world, I personally look for a solid foundation. And for that, I follow the Psalmist of Israel:

*I love You, Lord my strength,*
*The Lord is my rock and my fortress*
*and my deliverer; My God, my rock in*
*whom I take refuge . . .*
Psalm 18:1-3 NIV

Therein is a castle that does not change with the times. A Word that withstands all undulating sentiments.

# Heart-stopping, Part Één

The train raced on its way toward us; try as it might, it never outpaces the dawn.

It's 6:30 a.m. on a Wednesday morning. The air of Northern France breathes quite well. the only hindrance to a beautiful experience is the smoke. However, this is no matter, as the olfactory senses it stimulates will serve me well as a memory bank. I need to have my memory jogged. Especially of this morning. Of this day.

Things unfold as soon as the train screeches to a halt in front of us. We climb aboard the local as our bleary, caffeine-deprived eyes grant us membership on the 6:45 train to Lille, France's 2nd largest metropolitan region. From there, half-an-hour on the TGV, the high-speed line, will drop us off in the capital of Belgium.

The pristine, manicured landscape we pass looks in on us. We are observed by the neat, rolling hills out-of-doors. What do they see? Not just the countryside of Northern France, but all the nations of Europe? Perhaps the continent views us as children who needed space to grow; thus we ran away from home some centuries ago. The terrain of Europe looks inside and wonders at urban-sprawl, houses made of fine wood, and trucks whose roars would shame the heartiest dragon. Our interiors make the out-of-doors hum with speculation and wonder.

Or, perhaps, that noise I hear is only the sound of train wheels slowing to a halt. Out roll the passengers, a vomit of hurry and focus—the only attributes people who ride public transportation possess. My friend and I amble along. He's been to Brussels before, but never in this part of the city. The sense of discovery sets us on equal playing fields. Only the advantage of speaking a local language, a talent my travelling companion possesses in spades, will get us from point A to point B.

The list of point B's is endless and enthralling:
- An entire museum devoted to Magritte.
- Many exhibits on the series *Tintin*
- A giant replica of an atom

113

- Chocolate!

Each and every venue promises excitement and vivid experiences.

Our tour of the Capital of the European Union begins well-enough, with a visit to a majestic tower.

This particular ancient edifice we find ourselves enclosed in is old. Very old. To prove its antiquity, a beautiful display of artifacts greets us

These public time-capsules reach inside and pull us into the centuries past. And then there were the stairs:

Magnificent marble altars! Practical and beautiful, as only Europe can produce. Onward, ever upward they climb.

They reach into the skies of Belgium, inviting us to ascend Valhalla as the gods in Das Rheingold do. Invitations this long-standing are not to be snubbed.

And, when the view is from this point of reference, we would be most impolite to refuse.

July 1, 2014

# Heart-stopping, Part Twee

"FEET, don't fail me now!"

If my feet could express themselves emotionally, they would not be too pleased with the amount of walking Brussels demands.

"It's the world's second-smallest continent," I snark at their whines. "You can handle this."

Their reply is cold, unfeeling.

But, when in Europe, the best sights and sites will be found by foot. Cathedrals in their holy splendor, museums with all of history spread before you, bistros and shops from which to sample delicacies. All of these are best accessed with those beautiful tools with which the Maker equipped our legs. And so, our tour of Brussels continues à pied.

Along the way, icy-cold glowers of imposing edifices stare us into submission—

Along the way, time is told in the most European fashion—

Along the way those that walked these hallowed streets before us, wish us Godspeed—

Each city beckons us with feelings and auras unique to that place. These are the strings that move the marionettes we politely dub "tourists." All notions of autonomy are illusory.

Of course, walking, talking, and gawking take on added dimensions when the rest of the world revolves 'round you, caught in its daily tracks and spheres of influence. The language barrier only isolates us further.

However, the city is pleasant.

At one point, we pass a cathedral and I swear I hear music as though piped through its sound system.

I am disillusioned when we pass a man on a street corner making glorious music solely with the aid of his vocal chords. No artificial recordings need apply.

Continuing on, we stumble across the main part of town.

The electric current pulsing through the city's downtown region gently shocks us. Gradually, the amps get turned up and we are on fire. Soon enough, we find ourselves drinking in every ounce of culture permeating the streets.

We imbibe the rich nectar of the clothing shops.

We slowly absorb the beautiful language.

We eat well.

Satiated, we walk on.

When in Belgium, eat a waffle. I don't think they let you leave without one.

Seafood and chocolate. Seafood and chocolate. These two sellers alternate, leaving a zebra-striped appearance to the city. But we don't mind the monotony.

We thus spent many an hour in village pubs, sampling the ale while he charmed the locals with his genuine interest in all things English.

*Jon-Mark Grussenmeyer*

I think laughing with someone is a significant way to earn their trust. That's what David and I did. We trusted each other.

*Diana Hoffman*

## The Grief That Sees A Star
### Introduction to *Diana's Song*, by Diana Hoffman

"Were you born a poor, black child?"

It's a seemingly inappropriate question to ask anyone, let alone someone clearly Caucasian. But not if making a reference to David Lord's Steven Martinesque-circa—*The Jerk*—comedic style.

David and I went to school together, but being a few classes apart, didn't really meet until we joined the Pageant Wagon Players, a small troupe of talented actors producing summer melodrama comedies from 2005 through 2009.

Oh, how he made me laugh with his awkward physical comedy, facial expressions, sound effects, and dry one-liners. One of my favorite things was when he and I would both attempt to make the other crack-up while trying to maintain as stoic an expression as possible. He was usually the victor, but I'd have my moments, too. He'd turn bright red, lower his head with a tight-lipped smile, then rock his head back uttering a hearty "ho-ho" whilst clapping his knee.

I think laughing with someone is a significant way to earn their trust. That's what David and I did. We trusted each other.

As we grew closer, David let me in to some of his less funny thoughts and struggles. He referred to me as his cool big sister. When he was away at school there were nights when he'd call me, the giants being too hard to wrestle on his own. I always tried to coax him out of his room, encouraging him to take a walk with me. Sometimes he'd humor me, get out, and walk. We'd discuss what we saw surrounding us on the walk together.

Other times, I'd tell him I'd settle for him just opening a window and taking deep breaths with me while I strolled outside and described to him what I saw. At the time I didn't totally understand the depth of the battle David was immersed in. I always told him he was not alone and encouraged any movement he made toward truth and health, regardless of how small it seemed. I told him I admired his strength to meet with a counselor, as I, at that point, had not mustered up the courage to do so, myself.

When David sent me this story, he titled *Contacts* or *Diana's Song,* in 2009, it overwhelmed and moved me to realize how he viewed me. I asked him if he'd shared these thoughts with a counselor and he assured me he had.

One of my favorite Victor Hugo quotes pointing towards hope is, "he sought to transfer the grief that sees only a pit, into the grief that sees a star." It is that quote that often inspired me while talking with David. Hope.

Depression is like a cancer. Sometimes it goes into remission. Sometimes, with therapy and medicine, it can be managed. Other times, it rushes in with a fury and knocks the breath right out of you. I still have moments when I think, *what if he had called me that night when the fury rushed in?*

Then I remember some of our conversations when I'd tell him how close God was to the brokenhearted and that because God is so near, he is never alone. I allow my what-if thoughts to be replaced with the truth that, in David's most fury-riddled moments, God was present with him. God was near. David was not alone. He fell into the embrace of God with grace and love.

In my battles with depression and anxiety, I've often pulled out this story that David wrote to me in 2009—a year of many changes among all our coming-of-age friends. I've kept it hidden for years as something shared just between me and him. When I read through it again, I'm reminded to look up. To remember that I am not alone and that life in all its awful, awkward, beautiful, loveliness is worth digging in my heels, in hope, and fighting for.

As I wonder at how swiftly five years have passed without my friend, I know it is time to share this short story he entrusted to me with others who may need to hear Diana's Song.

# Diana's Song

The wheels grinded to a halt in their silent resting place along the gravel road of the nature preserve. He was not sure what brought him here. All he knew was that a silent scream outside his window awakened him and told him it was time. That this was his moment to prove to the world and to himself just the kind of mettle Roger Peterson was made of.

Roger's self-image continually sang its depressing siren song of *No Worth*. But tonight, with one final act of aggression, he would enter into the elite ranks of brave men.

*I believe my worth is based on others and my circumstances. THIS IS A FALSE BELIEF!*

He roamed through the woods along the nature trail with his friend in his hand and the silence that drove him to such desperation in his soul. There was no possible way of knowing the motivation behind his presence in the early morning mist. But he did know one thing. He knew that a great chasm had opened-up between humanity and his spirit. He could feel the cold, icy winds of a palace made of steel and granite, housing the people he so desperately cried out for but could not reach.

However, the outside looking in is never a view highly desired. Yes, he could identify this feeling of isolation, but this action he was about to take would forever cement his independence.

His search for the perfect tool to the purpose was fruitless until he encountered another friend in the clearing. Another friend he could implicitly trust. "Has anyone ever trusted you before?" He inquired of the large, knobby form, beginning his ascent toward the closest branch.

No answer. Perhaps this was the best reason his friend could be so trusted. No answer.

He was near his destination. The worn-out fibers of one friend met the old bark of the other in a macabre handshake that took the form of a knot. As he climbed down to pray, the cell phone in his pocket hit the ground, landing in an open position. "Dang," he muttered as he surveyed his friend, hoping no serious damage . . .

No! Hope was dead.

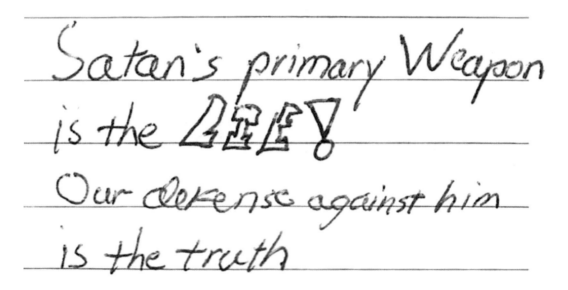

His phone was immaterial. Until—it began to shake. Not vibrate but convulse in a manner completely foreign. It not only shook but began to glow. It shone bright with a light not unlike that which Saul must have experienced upon the Damascus way—just before he met Jesus. The ethereal radiance beamed its way heavenward.

There, in the middle of the clearing among the shrubs and thickets stood a group of people. Not just any people, but his comrades. Many of his close companions. Even so, one or two were not immediately familiar to him until he suddenly recognized them. "You guys work in the deli!" he said. "You work at the library! Why, you're all the people in my contact list!"

It was true. Before his eyes stood the people on the contact list recorded in his cell phone. Surrounding him to the left and to the right, north and south were all those whose presence he found so necessary for daily survival. There they stood, wearing dark, depressed facial expressions. It reminded him of the rift separating him from the rest of his fellow humans. This fantastic occurrence only cemented what he already knew. It only gave him greater motivation for his purpose.

He climbed the makeshift scaffold with renewed vigor. Nothing would stop him now. He had seen those he trusted and found nothing to respond to. It was time to finish what he had started. This would have been easy except for a voice crying from the midst of his contacts.

"How can you do such a selfish thing?" the voice demanded from among the crowd, halting the machine driving him.

He stopped. He thought. Thought long and hard over this objection. Then again proceeded to climb.

"You're about to hurt those you love more than you could ever imagine!" the voice embodied itself in the guise of a female figure stepping out from among those present. "In your dark fantasy, you end, and you think the pain of those you love ends too. But I'm here to tell you it's not so black and white."

"Over time you will heal," Roger intoned with matter-of-fact diffidence. "You will heal."

"No, we will smooth over the love we have for you so we can function, but there will always be a gaping hole, just your dimensions, in our souls."

Another pause echoed through the woods. Another few steps up the gallows.

"Look around you. If you look hard enough, you may see past your self-pity—and see life. Look past yourself for once!" the voice demanded.

The inanimate faces grew concerned and waved hands at her in a disciplinary manner, hoping to quiet the rampage. But there was no stopping her. Her lust for life throbbed in sync with the beat of her heart. She was not going to see another senseless act of aggression take place just because some people fearfully skated around the hard sayings.

"Just look at things changing. The birds are migrating through, the ferns are growing, the rabbits are mating." The voice softened, still ripe with determination.

Roger did look around. He saw past himself. He saw the flowers bloom, the sun rise, the birds procreate. Life was beginning to sing, and Roger's ears started tuning out the silence. Suddenly, the fortress that held his loved ones warmed, and a bridge erected itself calling him to cross. Only two more steps towards final justice.

"Rog—" the voice pleaded. "ROG!" It screamed with all the passion it could muster. "You're changing, and you're not happy with it. I changed, and I didn't know what to make of it either, but there are people who want to help."

Silence.

"I want to help." The voice grew clearer.

Music suddenly rang around Roger calling him to muster with respect. He saw himself in his cradle with his mother singing an old folksong to put him to sleep. The music ringing within him melted into a duet with his mother's voice. He heard it again, seeing himself as valedictorian claiming his prize in a speech during graduation. It out sang *Pomp and Circumstance*. He felt the song as his grandmother breathed her last. Even then the song reminded him that it was not a one-sided ditty. It was a beating, loud, violent song, one that had gripped humanity throughout the ages. It has to be loud. It has a good deal of silence to break through.

Roger stepped down. His role as executioner was no longer necessary. He picked up his cell phone, and the specters that had haunted the clearing faded into the gray mist as a deer might disappear into the forest. He broke down and cried for several minutes.

When he came to, he took his pocket-knife and carved the name Diana in the large, bark-covered friend. He did it in honor of her music. Her siren song. The song mankind has sung since it fell flat on its face in Paradise. He left his friends in their place and moved on.

You can walk through those woods today, you know. And if you listen closely, you'll hear *Diana's Song*. It rings with a vibrato unknown to mere human voice and experience, sending shivers up your spine. From there it mixes with the song of the universe, ringing out loud and clear for those who will just hold on. Hold on!

And in some places, the song even drowns out the silence.

> *It is imperative to your Growth and getting Spiritual maturity that you understand God's truth about who you are.*

***Editor's Note:*** *David's lifetime struggled in this battle, ultimately succumbed to the devil and his inner critic's song of "no worth" despair to win out over Diana's Song and the Song of the Universe— the song of love and connection to others. We, however, can make a different choice, as Roger did in this story. Roger, representing David, overcame the temptation to make the final, dark choice of "justice" for his perceived failings. His connection to those around him made a difference in helping him overcome, as he did many times in his life. If someone around you wrestles with the song of their condemning inner critic, empathize with their pain and help them hear their own Diana's Song. God's grace and love, reflected through you, may help them chose life. The images included here are excerpts the Devotional Journal of David Lord, 2009.*

PART TWO:

At the Intersection
of Depression
and Suicide

He looked at me intently and replied, "You were right. The fact that he got saved in the end made it easier to play. If he had no future, I don't think I could have done it."

*Pastor Russell Sterger*

# In Retrospect of Life
## By Pastor Russell Sterger

I met David Lord through a Christian drama production written and directed by a friend named Kathryn Ross. I had seen him perform in other productions, namely the Pageant Wagon Players Old-Fashioned Melodrama Summer Theatre comedies. They were fun and amusing and he seemed cut out for the "everyman" kind of character.

However, I came to know him better when I was actually in a production with him—a comedy titled *Kit-n-Kaboodles* (pictured above) and a more serious drama featuring a light verses darkness theme.

In retrospect, David was a mystery to me—like a character out of a Sherlock Holmes novel riddled with clues, all of them hard to piece together. I thought it appropriate that we'd meet while doing a Christian drama with a hint of mystery undermining it.

Through the process of rehearsal, Kathryn (who wrote the script in production) and I realized there was a scene missing. Such is often the case with original works. It takes time to flesh out the story with the actors in place before one can fully bring all the pieces together. Stepping back from it midway through, we decided the play needed a scene with a darker tone, drawing out the full scope of the conflict in order for the light, or revelation, to have greater impact. The show needed a scene to more boldly represent a central truth: No matter how far anyone may have drifted from God, no one is beyond salvation. Kathryn saw I had a vision for it and recommended I write this key scene.

The play revolved around the biblical account of the Gadarene demoniac recorded in Matthew 8. As it stood, David portrayed the central character who would be demonically possessed, drawn away by a lust for greed and power. His decline into the abyss was not addressed directly—only referred to by the other characters. His possession took place offstage and only the results of it were seen onstage.

I added a scene where David played one of the two demon possessed men, working through the temptation to give into the dark side of his nature as seduced by the older possessed man, played by myself. The demon inside the older man used all sorts of tricks to bring him to the dark side, a la Darth Vader.

It was a powerful and dramatic scene made more powerful by the fact that both men were rescued and saved in the end by none other than Jesus Himself.

> *When Jesus arrived on the other side of the lake, in the region of the Gadarenes two men who were possessed by demons met him. They lived in a cemetery and were so violent that no one could go through that area. They began screaming at him, "Why are you interfering with us, Son of God? Have you come here to torture us before God's appointed time?" So the demons begged, "If you cast us out, send us into that herd of pigs." "All right, go!" Jesus commanded them. So the demons came out of the men and entered the pigs, and the whole herd plunged down the steep hillside into the lake and drowned in the water. The herdsmen fled to the nearby town, telling everyone what happened to the demon-possessed men. Then the entire town came out to meet Jesus, but they begged him to go away and leave them alone.*
>
> Matthew 8:28-34 NLT

In my former theatrical career, I'd played parts like this often, from Shakespeare to Orwellian dramas. Even so, this was different and uniquely challenging.

As up for the task as I felt myself to be, David, on the other hand, struggled in the role. This was especially evident as he wrestled with his lines—something that he'd never had difficulty in before. As rehearsals continued, I realized something else was going on. He battled playing this emotional level of a dramatic type and confided in me that he had never played a character so complicated before. He feared he could not do it justice.

I reassured him that, not only could he play the part well, but his very innocence would add depth to it. Especially later on when the Lord rescues him from evil and brings him into the light of salvation.

But he didn't seem quite convinced.

During one of our rehearsals, David pulled me aside and said, "I'm not doing a very good job with this—am I?"

I reminded him that it was a difficult scene for any actor, but I thought he was doing well. "In fact," I said, "I don't know anyone else who could do it as well as you are."

He shook his head. "I just don't want to let anyone down."

Putting my hand on his shoulder, I said, "Just put your heart into it and it will be wonderful."

He half-heartedly nodded his head. "I guess so."

There was something in the way he replied that struck me. I remember thinking later that this young man seemed plagued by a desire to always want to please everyone. He desired to do things perfectly, not make any mistakes, and to never let anyone down.

Unfortunately, I didn't know him well enough to realize the depth of his struggle.

As we finished our final performance, I pulled David aside to encourage him. "I told you that you could do it. The scene went perfect! Everyone was extremely moved by it."

He looked at me intently and replied, "You were right. The fact that he got saved in the end made it easier to play. If he had no future, I don't think I could have done it."

Being a pastor, these words resonated with me. Clearly, to David, Christian salvation was not just a concept to be lightly addressed, but something very important to his core self.

I shook his hand and said, "Amen, David. That was the point of the scene. That no one is beyond God's redemption no matter how lost he may feel on the inside."

He shifted his head to one side, smiled a forced smile at best, and thanked me. I had the sense that he did not understand the gift he possessed—not just to be able to entertain people with his comedic gifts, but to move them. Deeply. As I walked away, I remember thinking that even though it seemed forced, it was one of the few times I'd ever remembered seeing him smile.

Hindsight is a funny thing. It leaves us scratching our heads, wondering if there was more we could've done in a moment we only realized as opportune much later. Was there more I could have added in that exchange? If only I'd tried to be closer to him, to understand the depth of his dilemma better. Perhaps I could have helped him. Perhaps I could have persuaded him otherwise if he had made a call to me when struggling in a dark place. But we didn't have that kind of relationship. There always seemed a wall built up around him, difficult to penetrate. I didn't have a clue.

Some people suggest that suicide is a selfish act. Perhaps, in some cases, it is. Especially when an individual focuses predominately on their inner pain and a desire to end it, displaying a disconnect with those left behind. Yet with David, it was clearly an act of desperation. Of rampant discouragement. In my mind anyway, it seemed he simply didn't feel he belonged here.

Yet for those of us who knew him, nothing could be further from the truth. He did belong here. He did impact those around him in unnumbered, positive and life-giving ways. What a surprising and senseless loss. His life did have meaning.

For David, the struggle for meaning is over. For the rest of us, it lingers.

And yet why should we be surprised that the search for meaning in our lives holds such power over us? This world bombards our young people on a daily basis with its media-driven message that life has little value. Over and over, from all directions we are openly and imperceptibly being brainwashed into a growing sense of hopelessness. That Creation itself is nothing more than the result of randomness. That the beauty of nature and the wildlife David loved so much is merely the result of a cosmic or biological accident. What does a confused mind do with such misinformation?

This assault of chaos and turmoil on ordered thought leaves people to wonder where their value really lies. Somewhere along the way, David lost a sense of his own self-worth and his value to others. Somewhere along his path, a dark inner voice led him to make an erroneous turn. It seemed an illness took him.

I was not ill when I met David. In fact, as far as I can remember, I've never been really sick a day in my life. At least not sick enough to spend the night in the hospital.

By the time I met David I had traveled to 18 different countries, ministered in war-torn areas, and brought food and medical supplies to two regions devastated by natural disaster. To quote one of my favorite television shows, I always felt compelled to "boldly go where no man had gone before." My desire to travel to dangerous places was predicated upon the fact that I was single, had no children, and was in a position to go where others might be hesitant to consider.

I remember asking David if he'd ever thought about going on one of my crazy mission trips. He just shook his head as if astonished that anyone would even ask him such a thing. I wasn't close enough to David to press the subject, so I let it go. I believe it's unfortunate that he never got to experience that kind of missionary endeavor. But then again that is retrospect, which is very often in the eye if the beholder.

In retrospect of my own life, I should have taken better care of the testing and cancer screening available to me. By the time the results of my colonoscopy came back, my oncologist said it was too late. Some even suggested I only had less than six months to live.

This kind of news to someone who had never been sick in their life is devastating, to say the least. Following the diagnosis, the months ahead plunged me into a world of tests and surgeries and more tests and chemotherapy and more surgeries. Six months went by and I was still here. To everyone's surprise.

To everyone's surprise—except mine. I determined that whatever time I had left I was going to use it to encourage others. To encourage them to stay strong in the Lord, no matter what their circumstances.

It may sound trite but being a pastor of a church and having so many people praying for me, it seemed only natural that I should want to give back in any way I knew how. And quite frankly the only way I knew how to give back was to stay strong, and not let my circumstances drag me into the darkness of my own fears.

As much as I'd like to feign being a saint or a martyr through it all, there have been times when I was so sick that I actually asked God to take me home. To relieve me from my suffering. It would have been very easy to reach over and empty a bottle of pills and drift off into permanent darkness. However, I knew that if I could not end my life on my own terms.

My life does not belong to me. It belongs to God. And it always will. This reality has kept my head above water on many occasions. Such insight reminds me that my life is in His hands and it is up to Him how much longer I remain on this earth. However, the determination of what I will do with the remaining time of my life is up to me.

It's now been four years since that initial diagnosis of less than six months. I bear this in mind when my doctors become too adamant about one treatment over another. It's not been easy. There have been times when I was so sick it took great courage just to get up in the morning. But I had a reason to get up. I had a reason to keep going. And I think that's what's important in this life—especially when difficulties and hardships enter into them.

David was not a coward. Some people suggest that suicide is a coward's way out. I believe David had struggles that went beyond such simple platitudes. For example, it took great courage for him to stand up and give nature talks to complete strangers. Or to play difficult parts in dramatic productions. He was not a coward by any means. He simply, in my mind anyway, became overwhelmed, lost in wandering.

Somewhere along the line, perhaps David lost his understanding of how valuable he was or could be to people. He forgot how encouraging it is to others to see someone battling illness, whatever it might be, with strength and fortitude.

There are those who may be reading this who themselves have forgotten how important they are in the grand scheme of things. To those I would encourage you to remind yourself that every day is precious. Every moment is an opportunity to minister to others. And every hardship is an opportunity to help others define strength, even when they feel they are on their last legs.

All of us who knew David wish we could have done more. For those of us who remain, David's legacy still teaches us. Our job is to embrace closely the people around us and encourage those who struggle in their way. We do this by our life, by our testimony and by the hope that lives within us.

In one way or another, we all have some form of a wall built around us to protect where we are most vulnerable. We all possess some level of ourselves in a shroud of mystery. Sometimes we are so well hidden that even a master detective might miss the clues to sleuthing us out to help us find our solutions.

But we can try. We can live our lives perceptive enough to recognize when clues are right in front of us. We can summon the courage to love. To risk relationship. To pray for the clue—the key—that opens the door in the wall where we can encourage others to fully embrace their life worth living.

***Editor's Note:*** *Pastor Russell Sterger lost his battle with cancer on June 25, 2019, a mere four months after writing this chapter. Those of us who knew his passion to embrace the adventure of engaging every corner of the world with God's potential for living out the gift of life to the fullest, will miss him, as we miss our mutual friend, David Lord. Pastor Russ' words in this chapter leave a legacy of truth for all—no matter the battles we face his retrospect on life provides an example well worth emulating in the time we have. Now, in eternity, David and Russ are together again.*

Every day is precious. Every moment is an opportunity to minister to others. And every hardship is an opportunity to help others define strength, even when they feel they are on their last legs.

The only way I knew how to give back was to stay strong, and not let my circumstances drag me into the darkness of my own fears.

How encouraging it is to others to see someone battling illness, whatever it might be, with strength and fortitude.

I determined that whatever time I had left I was going to use it to encourage others. To encourage them to stay strong in the Lord, no matter what their circumstances.

**Russell Sterger, February 2019**
Chapter excerpts from *He Wondered as He Wandered—In Retrospect*

*Photo Credit: The photos used in this chapter are used by permission of Violet Brown Photography.*

Look at the birds. They don't plant or harvest or store food in barns, for your heavenly Father feeds them. And aren't you far more valuable to him than they are?
Matthew 6:26 NLT

*Pastor Frank Ippolito*

# From Darkness to Light
## By Pastor Frank Ippolito

*"None of us began that week expecting to be at a funeral. Nobody ever wants to go to a funeral, yet there we were. Naturally, we would have rather been somewhere else—anywhere else, but at a funeral. And, definitely, none us could have imagined that we would have been attending the funeral of our friend and loved one, David Lord."*

That's how I began my Eulogy for David's memorial on that October day. I went on to quote from the wise King Solomon in Ecclesiastes 7:2-4: *Better to spend your time at funerals than at festivals. After all, everyone dies—so the living should take this to heart. Sorrow is better than laughter, for grief and loss have a refining influence on us. A wise person thinks a lot about death, but only a fool thinks that just having a good time is what life is about.*

Then I went on to say, "None of us began that week expecting to be at a funeral. Nobody really wants to go to a funeral, yet here we are. But, since we're here—at a funeral—perhaps we can take some things to heart. Things that will have a refining influence on us."

Please allow me a moment or two to reminisce about my friend, David Lord.

I first met David many years ago in my church through the drama ministry of Kathryn Ross. David was his usual timid and unassertive self when I was first introduced to him. But it didn't take long before I got to know him and appreciate a deeper side to his personality.

The drama team had a huge influence on him. Acting seemed to draw him out of his shell and turn him into an entirely different person. In fact, he actually became creatively funny. You couldn't help but notice that he had an amazing memory, a gift of comedic humor, and a knack for dramatic timing. I enjoyed watching him perform in those plays and, to me, he will always be a star.

Yet, I still didn't know him all that well. He was always on stage, which typically meant he was performing and pretending to be someone else. I think he enjoyed making people laugh and moving us in some emotional way while he was on stage. It wasn't until he moved in with my wife and me for a season that we really got to know him and appreciate him and his real personality.

David was always so kind, polite, considerate, and very different in almost every way. I'll never forget the first time he wandered out of his bedroom and sat down at our kitchen table wearing his "little boy pajamas," as I called them. We had a few laughs about that—at his expense—and he laughed along with us. One time he went camping with some of the guys from our church. He stepped out of the camper wearing his "little boy" PJ's and joined the fellows around the campfire. They all had a pretty good laugh and gave David a good ribbing.

While David lived with us, he introduced us to his knowledge of birds, developing our awareness of the abundant nature around us that we never even realized was there. I can honestly say that I don't think we will ever be the same—and I don't think I'm alone in that sentiment. He enjoyed sharing his love of nature, especially his knowledge and passion for birds. I have an image burned in my memory of him teaching my youngest grandchildren all about the birds, their habits and habitats. He taught us to recognize birds we never noticed before in our backyard by the different calls they made. We remain so thankful to David for that and will never forget him because of it.

I'm also extremely grateful that we were able to see and experience his tenderness and infectious smile. He had a beautiful smile! When he smiled his entire face smiled with him; not only did his mouth smile, but his eyes and his entire face smiled, too. When he laughed, you couldn't help but laugh with him because you knew he was very happy.

David had an incessant and inquisitive mind, resulting in hours of late-night discussions. I believed him to be an intelligent young man with an old soul, as they say. We'd often chat way into the late-night hours during the nine months he lived with us, discussing theological subjects and difficult Bible passages. That's when I began to realize how tortured David really was inside and how his incessant and inquisitive mind was more than a brilliant mind. It was, in many ways, his worst enemy. It was part of a darkness within that he sought to escape from.

David struggled with deep depression. He often bounced between extreme happiness and deep sadness. Every one of us will experience some level of depression in life, from time to time. In fact, funerals are notorious for that. Typically, if you suffer the loss of a loved one or a friend, you'll naturally become depressed. At least for a while.

Of course, there are many life events that can bring about depression. Being unemployed will do it. For some, being single will do it, while, for others, being married will have the same effect. Disappointed with the outcome of a life's plan or goals that didn't quite meet our imagined expectations bring depression for some in life. It's possible to suffer from minor depression for any number of reasons.

These bouts with minor depression are considered normal and such experiences are usually only temporary. However, many people from all walks of life will struggle with major depression. Statistics show that "Major depressive disorder affects almost 15 million American adults in a given year—that's about 7 percent of the U.S. population age 18 and older." (*Archives of General Psychiatry*, 2005 Jun; 62(6): 617-27)

This tells us that depression is a serious problem in our society. In fact, it's possible—even probable—that some of you reading this book might be struggling with severe depression and you've been struggling for some time. If so, I would urge you to please seek help. Depression can often be relieved with proper care and sometimes with proper medications. Depression becomes especially dangerous when it remains in the dark and goes untreated.

Most depression in the normal variety can be, and usually is, remedied with a little bit of time and properly applied rational thought—more specifically, spiritual thought. Medication doesn't always have to be the first line of defense.

The Bible doesn't shy away from the subject of depression. King David, who was considered a spiritual and godly man, struggled with depression from time to time. In Psalm 42, a psalm attributed to David, the King did us a great service by recording one of his bouts with depression. He even provided a few details on how he fought against it:

> *My tears have been my food day and night,*
> *while all day long people say to me,*
> *"Where is your God?"*
> *My heart is breaking as I remember how it used to be:*
> *I walked among the crowds of worshipers,*
> *leading a great procession to the house of God,*
> *singing for joy and giving thanks amid the sound of a great celebration!*
> *Why am I depressed? Why is my heart so sad?*
> *I will put my hope in God! I will praise him again—my Savior and my God.*
> *I am deeply depressed; therefore, I remember You . . .*
> *My adversaries taunt me, as if crushing my bones,*
> *while all day long they say to me, "Where is your God?*
> *Why am I so depressed? Why is this turmoil within me?*
> *Put your hope in God, for I will still praise Him, my Savior and my God.*
>
> Psalm 42:3-11

The point, here, is that it's even possible for a deeply spiritual person to be depressed.

There are two primary effects of depression: hopelessness and helplessness. Both are powerful enemies in one's battle with depression. So long as we're feeling or entertaining thoughts of hopelessness and helplessness, then we're going to be wedged against the ropes, as it were, and we'll be at risk of drowning in it.

It is when we bring it to the light, or talk about it with someone, that we can have better success in fighting it. Prayer is a way of talking about it—simply talking to God. So, in effect, prayer is a great way to bring the problem to light.

King David was influenced by what others were saying. He felt lonely and abandoned; he was overly fixated on his problems, his situation, and too focused on the negative people surrounding him as referenced above in Psalm 42: *"Where is your God [they would say to him]?" My heart is breaking as I remember how it used to be . . . My adversaries taunt me, as if crushing my bones."*

This sounds like crushing oppression from negative influences.

When we feel that way—when it seems as if we're standing on the mental doorway to melancholy—then we need to act fast. We need do something to interrupt the thought process. That's what King David did. He attacked his depression. He interrupted his thought pattern. He adjusted his focus. Note his response in verses 5-6: *"Why am I depressed? Why is my heart so sad? I will put my hope in God! I will praise him again—my Savior and my God. I am deeply depressed; therefore, I will remember You . . ."*

It was an intentional effort to change his focus by changing what and how he was thinking. Prayer and meditation on Scripture will help you do that.

I'm fairly certain that this approach will work for most of us at levels of normal depression. But there are those times when depression is more stubborn and more difficult. In such times, we have to fight even harder and be more creative. In such times, it takes all the strength we have to remember the Lord. The darkness is so dark that even the light of God is hard to see. But it's a choice that we must make—even though it's not easy—if we hope to survive the war.

We mustn't lose hope because our hope is in the Lord. Our help is best when it comes from the Lord. King David trained himself to lift his eyes toward his divine Helper. Psalm 121:1-3 says, *"I lift my eyes toward the mountains. Where will my help come from? My help comes from the LORD, the Maker of heaven and earth. He will not allow your foot to slip; He who watches over you will not slumber."*

We see from this psalm that there's often a struggle to maintain a spiritual focus. The battle is real—but so is our Helper.

In Lamentations 3:24, the prophet Jeremiah said, *"I say to myself, "The LORD is my inheritance; therefore, I will hope in him!"* Here is an important point that needs to be made: the prophet spoke to himself. Very often, depression comes as result of bad thoughts— wrong thinking—or an undisciplined mind. Quite simply, I'm not talking to myself in the right way. I'm listening to dumb, depressing, and dangerous ideas that originate within my own head. So, I need to disrupt my own thought patterns. I need to learn to talk to myself in a better way and stop listening to the wrong stuff.

That's the method that the psalmist and the prophet used. They both talked to themselves. They both made corrective arguments with their own minds and said the right things that redirected their wrong thinking. The psalmist said to himself, *"Why am I depressed? Why is my heart so sad? I will put my hope in God! I will praise him again!"* The prophet said to himself, *"The LORD is my inheritance; therefore, I will hope in him!"* In that way, they were able to thwart the wrong thoughts and introduce the right thoughts. So, it's good, helpful, and even necessary to talk to yourself. But in the right way.

This method may not be suitable to tackle the worst kind of depression, especially the clinical kind, but it certainly couldn't hurt to add this weapon to your spiritual arsenal. At the very least, this method is a good place to start fighting the battle. But it requires spiritual thinking. Even more than that, it requires biblical thinking. If this method isn't successful, then please seek the help of a professional, a friend, or a loved one. Don't try to fight this battle alone.

None of us were expecting to be at a funeral that October morning. We especially weren't expecting to be at David Lord's funeral. But, even by his untimely death, David was able to shed some light on an important subject—one that was always there, but we were mostly unaware of it until that day. David exposed us to a silent and dangerous condition called, depression. And, of course, he also exposed us to depression's very close companion—suicide.

We know where our David is now, we have no doubt; the Bible assures us with great clarity. Those who believe in Jesus will have a home in heaven with Christ. We know it—we're sure of it—and that gives us hope. Jesus confirms this truth as recorded in John 11:25. *"I am the resurrection and the life. He who believes in Me, though he may die, he shall live."*

David's earthly journey has come to an end—but his eternal reality has only just begun. This life was hard for him, but his new life is a breeze.

That's the hope we have in Christ. And, that's why it's *"Better to spend your time at funerals than at festivals. After all, everyone dies—so the living should take this to heart. Sorrow is better than laughter, for grief and loss have a refining influence on us. A wise person thinks a lot about death, but only a fool thinks that just having a good time is what life is about."* (Ecclesiastes 7:2-4).

We would do well to take these things to heart for they may have a refining influence upon us.

If you're experiencing depression, today, and are unable to get control of it—if you're thinking of hurting yourself in any way—then please seek help from someone who is trained and able to help you. The Lord is always there to help you in all areas of your life, but He often puts trained professionals in our lives to assist us along the way. Please, reach out for the help you need.

I miss David. I miss his smile. I miss the talks we had. I miss his brilliant and insightful mind. I miss watching him perform. I miss that we won't get to see what he might have become in this world. His absence has left a hole in our hearts and lives. But David has reached the place of perfection that he always strived for. The Bible tells us that we will be as perfect as Jesus is perfect when we finally reach heaven.

Perfection is the future condition of every believer.

David looked forward to heaven, although, he rushed it a bit and took matters into his own hands. I don't recommend that anyone follow his lead in that way.

But I think his actions show us the extreme depth of darkness and pain that David battled and that he struggled in his thought life. Therefore, one of the purposes in compiling this book about David Lord is to help others who may be burdened by depressive and suicidal thoughts. We want to help.

While it's true that David taught my family and me a lot about birds, he taught me much more about life. His legacy is LIFE!

I can't wait to see him again.

**Editor's Note:** *The Scripture verses included in this chapter are either a paraphrased version by the author or a combination of different translations.*

While it's true that David taught my family and me a lot about birds, he taught me much more about life. His legacy is LIFE!

*Pastor Frank Ippolito*

At the center, we need the light of Jesus Christ, who is the King of Kings and Lord of Lords.

*Dr. Ronald Newman*

## Seeking Balance
### By Dr. Ronald Newman

I've experienced the loss of several loved ones by means of suicide in my lifetime. When a loved one takes their life, we are prone to second guess every interaction we had with them. The temptation to beat ourselves up for things we did not do causes us to wrestle with nagging thoughts that we might have prevented the tragedy. In terminal circumstances, life does not give us a do-over.

In this chapter, I share some best practices for those battling depression and an addiction to perfectionism, which often plays into the self-loathing and despair that puts one at risk for suicidal tendencies. In the wake of a loved one's loss, grief fills the void in the hearts of those left behind. This is a normal element in the cycle of human emotions we all must endure for a season. I share some helpful tips to steering a healthy course through grief's stormy waters. Finally, I list a few suggestions for growing more aware of suicidal behaviors, so you can be pro-active in helping someone you love through a turbulent season in their life and give them the support they may need to find healing.

### Dark Valleys of Depression

*Yea, though I walk through the valley*
*of the shadow of death,*
*I will fear no evil; For You are with me;*
*Your rod and Your staff, they comfort me.*
Psalm 23:4 NKJV

Depression is everyman's illness. It strikes people who then experience a loss of interest or enjoyment in life, lack of energy, social withdrawal, feelings of worthlessness and hopelessness, and even suicidal thoughts. The causes may vary including loss in one's life, trauma in a person's past, unhealthy family relationships, or even genetic and generational predispositions. Throughout the books of Job and Psalms in the Bible, depression is expressed in gut wrenching emotional language illustrating that in every age and across cultures, men and women have struggled with this emotion.

If you struggle with depression or know someone who does, the following suggestions are meant as inspiration toward successful coping approaches. Isaiah 26:3 NKJV that "You will keep him in perfect peace, whose mind is stayed on You, because he trusts in You." Consider carefully how applying these truths to life can equip those battling depression with the tools to climb out of the dark valleys and find balance in the light, landing on solid ground.

**Treat yourself with compassion.** Self-hate is often your enemy. Show yourself the compassion you would show someone else going through a similar struggle.
~ Reflection: Colossians 3:12; Matthew 9:36

**Tone down your inner critic.** Related to the above suggestion, this involves tuning in to what your negative, critical inner voice is saying, then turning down the volume. Simultaneously, you can tune in to the positive encouraging coach voice in your head and turn that volume up.
~ Reflection: Philippians 4:8; II Cor. 5:21

**Resist guilt and shame.** Accept their existence in your life but resist dwelling on these emotions. Instead, let go of the root cause of these feelings and focus on what is more important and of value to you. Forgiveness of others, and yourself, helps you make healthy changes in your behavior that can keep you moving forward.
~ Reflection: I John 1:9; Romans 8:1

**Activate yourself.** Resist the temptation to become more passive. Find those baby steps that keep you doing activities you used to find meaningful. Believe that you have the power to do this, even when you do not feel like doing anything. Ideally, increasing exercise in your life and eating in a healthy manner can be part of this activation.
~ Reflection: I Peter 1:13; Matthew 25:31-46; I Corinthians 9:24-27; Proverbs 24:30-34

**Avoid spiritualizing the problem.** Many people of faith beat up on themselves for not having enough faith, or praying enough, or doing some other spiritual discipline or exercise. This only makes the depression worse. Focus on the emphasis of grace in your faith-tradition and seek strength to deal with the areas of life where making different choices benefits you.
~ Reflection: Galatians 1:6-9; Gal. 3:1-5; Gal. 5:1-6

**Get medical tests.** In some cases, depression is due to medical conditions, therefore these must be ruled out. This is particularly true when there is no clear situational explanation for the depression. Adrenal insufficiency, diabetes, thyroid problems, Lyme disease, anemia, sleep apnea, and lupus are just a few examples. Ask your family doctor for guidance on the appropriate steps to take.
~ Reflection: Luke 17:12-14; Proverbs 1:22; 2:1-4; I Tim. 5:23

**Hold on to hope.** Develop a belief and confidence that your emotional state is temporary, not permanent. This hopeful attitude can be nurtured through meditating on stories of hope, or perhaps movies that used to stimulate a good feeling in you. Be inspired by the people who have wrestled with depression and come out victorious. You can, too.
~ Reflection: Proverbs 13:12; Hebrews 6:19; Romans 5:1-5

**Avoid depressing stimuli.** Avoid viewing tragic movies or television programs. Stay away from depressing books. Stop replaying your own discouraging stories in your mind, unless it is for the purpose of finding a healthier way of looking at the situation. Does alcohol (a depressant) or substance abuse pull you further into a depressive mindset? You can begin to break free from these chains that keep you down in the valley by not making space for them in your life.
~ Reflection:  Proverbs 2:10-12; Prov. 22:3, Prov. 23:20-21, 29-35

**Build a healthy support system.** This may involve setting boundaries on others who are toxic and do more harm to you than good. Since no man is an island, we do need other people in our lives. Building healthy relationships is essential in overcoming depression. Disable any tendency to be passive-aggressive or hostile. Remain friendly with those who are your true support system.
~ Reflection: Hebrews 10:24-25; I John 1:7; Ecclesiastes 4:9-12

**Get professional help.** There is no shame in obtaining help from a professional who has studied depression and understands its dynamics. They can help with various approaches to breaking free from its clutches. Different areas of focus in counseling may include: working through the grief of past losses, identifying and addressing unhealthy thought processes, and building healthy communication patterns with others. To augment the benefits of psychotherapy, medication can be of help to some people.
~ Reflection: Proverbs 11:14; Galatians 6:1-2; Isaiah 9:6; II Timothy 2:1-2

## The Drive of Perfectionism

Perfectionism is addiction to an unattainable standard. Research shows it can kill you. It does this by isolating you and destroying healthy relationships in your life. If you do not master its rigid and relentless grasp over you, it will lead to unhappiness and frustration in all you do. Fulfilling work becomes workaholism. Healthy planning and foresight become obsessive worry. Body image concerns turn into compulsive exercise and diet programs, or even anorexia or bulimia nervosa.

Growing toward achievement of our goals can be like the growth of a garden, imperceptible as we watch it, but more obvious over time. Our desire for excellence can be harnessed as we challenge ourselves to avoid the pitfalls of perfectionism. If you struggle in this area, consider how the following tips can help you live a more balanced life:

**Identify specific goals.** Establish realistic goals that really matter, such as those involving your character and how you identify yourself. Be gracious toward yourself. Setting goals requires evaluating your flaws and mistakes, which requires honest humility. Target developing healthy habits, including the practice of self-control of how you think and act. Creating a plan for excellence needs to be balanced with acceptance of mistakes on your journey through life.

**Establish priorities for change.** What really matters to you? What matters to those you care about most? Focus on change within. Develop a healthier mind and body, rather than external concerns such as growing wealth. For example, a healthy foundation for improving your business is built when you focus first on building your character from the inside out.

**Identify perfectionistic thinking.** Where do you see inflexible and rigid thought patterns in your life? Where are you overly demanding with yourself or others? Do you notice a strong inner critic, a relentless, judgmental voice in your head? When you hear yourself say "should have" or "ought to," reevaluate your thinking. Make a log of all these thoughts so you can avoid them in the future.

**Find alternate healthy thought patterns.** All or nothing thinking, or black and white thoughts, must be modified to include life realities of grey patterns. Lessen the importance of your inner critic and embrace the voice of healthy coaches in your life. For example, instead of saying "This is awful, and I am a terrible parent" because of your child's misbehavior, think "It is sad my child misbehaved, but I will do what I can to develop consequences to teach him lessons from this situation."

**Find alternate healthy behavior patterns.** You cannot please everyone. Perfection is impossible in this life, even as we seek to do our best. Let go of your need for things to go your way, if you determine it is not working. Diminish the importance of mistakes you have made in the past. Restrain yourself from correcting every little mistake others make.

**Identify perfectionistic behaviors.** These grow from unconscious efforts to avoid something, such as difficult, painful relationships or memories. People may emphasize the need for power or competence over healthy connections with others, which block the ability to relax or enjoy inner peace. Seek balance by meditating on valued relationships.

**Embrace the usefulness of emotions.** Do you get angry when your rigid protocols are not followed? Are you depressed because of your perceived failures? Does fear paralyze you? Negative emotions alert us to areas in our thinking and behavior where we experience trouble. Recognize the signs and take heart that change is possible. The 17th century French poet and playwright Moliere said, "The greater the obstacle, the more glory in overcoming it."

**Master your fear—embrace courage.** Businessman, philanthropist, and author W. Clement Stone said, "Thinking will not overcome fear, but action will." Accept the experience of anxiety but overcome it by pressing through it toward your valued goal.

**Discover your power to change.** Freedom means we have the power of choice. We do not have to follow established patterns of habitual behavior. What feels normal to us does not need to be acted upon, particularly if it undermines healthy relationships.

**Reinforce your power to change.** Keep a journal of experiences where you have successfully accomplished your goals. Express gratitude toward those who helped you along your journey. Positive emotional experiences and accomplishments reinforce and point to future success.

Suicide rates are highest for men over age 69. However, it seems especially tragic when the young, who had their whole lives ahead of them, commit suicide. At any age, the aftermath of a loved one's decision to end their life is devastating for survivors. Wounds suffered initially feel numb before pain strikes with unexpected intensity. The injury may become infected, requiring a more complicated healing process. Though it can heal over time, a scar remains as a reminder of the heartache and loss endured.

For some, this type of wound never fully heals.

A friend whose young adult son unexpectedly died in his arms described the grief process as a spiral where you revisit various thoughts and feelings, often triggered by the most unexpected things such as a smell, object, or location.

Here are a few tips to help manage the grief in your life, or the lives of others, when navigating in the wake of a loved one's loss. Whether through suicide or another unexpected cause, a keen awareness of how human emotions process tragedy aids healing, restores a healthy perspective of life, and enables you to move forward in peace:

**Recognize the unique nature of your grief.** When we expect someone to die due to illness or age, it is usually easier to accept than when a person chooses to end their own life. Guilt complicates our hurt and emotional confusion, in addition to the sadness and anger we feel at the loss. Give yourself permission to fully grieve.

**Forgive your own empathy failures.** We look back and reflect on how we failed to see the depth of the inner battle our loved one experienced. Whether from their failure to share, or from our difficulties tuning in and truly listening to their emotional pain, we must learn to accept and let go of our guilt or shame over our own real or perceived insensitivities.

**Don't fight the feelings.** Acknowledge them and seek to learn from them. Profound sadness, deep anger, guilt, shame, anxiety, and other emotions can be confusing as you wrestle with them after a loss. Accept their presence. John 11:35 records Jesus weeping at the tomb of Lazarus. In Matthew 26:37-38 (NLT), when Jesus went to pray in the Garden of Gethsemane on the night of His betrayal before His crucifixion, He is "anguished and distressed . . . 'My soul is crushed with grief to the point of death . . .'"

**View feelings as reminders of your connection to the deceased.** Whether positive or negative, feelings mean you've cared deeply for the lost loved one. Allow yourself to remember the good times you shared to strengthen that connection.

**Read books on grief to help you process and accept your experience.** A few options I recommend are *A Grief Observed*, by C.S. Lewis, *Recovering from the Losses of Life* by H. Norman Wright, *Beyond Grief* by Carol Staudacher, and *Grief's Courageous Journey* by Sandi Caplan and Gordon Lang. In 2 Timothy 4:13 NLT, the well-read apostle Paul demonstrates the importance of reference materials to his ministry when he instructs Timothy to *"Also bring my books, and especially my papers."*

**Write the deceased a letter.** Include random thoughts, feelings, images, memories, or whatever helps you process your inner experience. Consider drafting it in the style of a good-bye letter. Share it with someone, if you choose, or reread it at a future time when your grief resurfaces, such as an anniversary or special date.

**Keep a journal.** Document lessons you learned from your relationship with the deceased. Write about the thoughts, feelings, memories, and positive things you gained from knowing this special person. (Editor's Note: The publication of this book of devotions by David Lord illustrates this tip well.)

**Make a photo album or scrapbook.** Emotionally process memories using visuals and images. Besides printed photos and paper books to organize your visual materials, digital tools such as Shutterfly and/or blogs, plus social media like Pinterest, Instagram, and Facebook, allow anyone to create and edit slide shows, online scrapbooks, or 3-D souvenirs of a person or event.

**Create a Memory Quilt.** Each piece of the quilt may represent a memory or aspect of the person's life. Individual pieces, made by those with a connection to the deceased, help a community of people or extended family support each other in grief.

**Carry a linking object.** Carry something in your pocket or pocketbook, such as a pin, necklace, or personal memento that holds a special meaning related to your loved one to remind you of your connection. This may be useful, at least, for a season in your life.

**Forgive yourself, if needed.** Did your loved one pass leaving unresolved conflict between you? Forgive yourself. The deceased may have already forgiven you. Whether they did or not, bring your unresolved burden before God to receive His forgiveness, and therein, grace to forgive yourself. Pray for the ability to forgive them if you become aware of lingering resentments from unsettled conflict.

**Talk to someone.** There is no substitute for human contact and sharing with a supportive person who cares. Galatians 6:2 reminds us to "Share each other's burdens, and in this way obey the law of Christ." It can be a professional, clergy, a friend, family member, or God through prayer. Grief support groups such as My Sister's Kids, a peer support group for kids and teens in South Jersey, are available for people of all ages. Many churches have grief support group meetings weekly to help in this critical time. Verbalizing your grief helps you work through the different stages involved in the process.

**Seek meaning and purpose for the future.** Finding some type of meaning in our loss alleviates the temptation to embrace despair. I found meaning when I determined to become a psychologist in order to help people who struggle emotionally or who are suicidal. I wanted to connect with them in a way that empowered them to resist the temptation to end their lives. Volunteer with organizations that provide suicide prevention strategies such as mental health associations, self-help groups, and even lay-counseling ministries within church communities. Using loss as a catalyst to improving life in your sphere of influence redeems tragedy in one life, that may allow another life to triumph.

## Personal Pro-active Steps to Suicide Awareness

Commit yourself to learning more about depression and suicide prevention for the sake of others. Learn the community resources in your area. Research shows the benefits of psychological treatment, so know the local options available. In addition, take the following pro-active steps to live with more awareness to how others around you may be suffering:

**Recognize the risk factors.** Depression is the number one mental health risk factor for suicide, along with prior suicide attempts. Other risk factors include the loss of close relationships by means of suicide, and deep grief through the loss of other significant relationships. Research shows that youth with less social connections or a lower sense of meaning and purpose have a higher rate of suicidal thoughts. Maltreatment as a child is a risk factor for suicide as an adolescent. Also, when people feel they are a burden to others, they are at risk.

**Watch for warning signs.** Take notice when someone gives away their prized possessions, withdraws from everyone, or shows drastic changes in behavior such as lack of personal hygiene. If they exhibit increased risk-taking behavior, like drug or alcohol abuse, beware. If they are preoccupied with death, or talk about suicide, recognize it as a warning sign.

**Know the safety nets.** Research where to refer a loved one you see struggling for help and hope. Psychiatric medications may be a safety net if psychotherapy is not working for someone. Every community has a crisis intervention hotline. Keep the number readily accessible. Inpatient mental health facilities help people through the dark days when suicide seems like a viable option to them.

**Fight the stigma of getting professional help.** Nearly half our population struggles with a psychological difficulty by the time they are age 55. Only a small percentage of them seek professional help. The majority of problems can be addressed, even though many are afraid of being labeled in some way. Use a professional resource to provide guidance or comfort during a time of personal crisis in your life or as an intervention in the life of another.

**Advice for the spiritually minded.** When ministering to someone who is suicidal, don't dissuade them from their fear of God's judgment. It might be the only barrier preventing them from taking their life. If someone has taken their life and you are ministering to their loved ones or need to find comfort yourself, focus on the mercy of God, not His judgement. Trust God who knows the beginning to the end. His mercies and love are eternal.

## In Conclusion

We all face challenges as individuals and together with others. Whether we like it or not, we are involved in spiritual warfare, and the enemy's purpose is to "kill, steal and destroy". He does this through deception, which is his primary power. We need one another so that we are not picked off by the one who is seeking to devour each of us. At the center, we need the light of Jesus Christ, who is the King of Kings and Lord of Lords.

If you know someone who is struggling, or if that someone is you, do not hesitate to seek consistent discipleship counseling from someone you trust. A mature Christian counselor can help you apply the Word of God to your life in practical ways as noted above.

Sources of potential counselors can be found on-line at:
www.christiancounselingsj.webs.com (for South Jersey); www.aacc.net or www.caps.net (nationally); or by calling Lighthouse Network at 844-543-3242 or 877-562-2565. If inpatient care is needed, Lighthouse Network can help with that as well.

If you are in need, you may be able to receive treatment from the caregivers at Honey Lake Clinic in Greensboro, Florida, or another facility that can help you overcome your troubles. If these resources aren't available and there are no large churches with caring ministries and people who can help, every county in the USA has a community mental health center, and emergency services to help when you are in a crisis. Calling for help is the first step in receiving the help you need.

**Editor's Note:** *All proceeds from the sales of this book benefit the NATIONAL SUICIDE PREVENTION LIFELINE, 1 800 273-8255.*
*Visit them online at www.suicidepreventionlifeline.org.*

PART THREE:

Tributes to
David's Life
and Legacy

If telling David's story through this book helps just one person . . . than it has been worth every tear I've shed.

*Amanda Lord Wojcik*

**Thankful**
**By Amanda Lord Wojcik**

*"The person who completes suicide dies once. Those left behind die*
*a thousand deaths trying to relive those terrible moments and understand . . . Why?"*
Sheila E. Clark and Robert D. Goldney
*The Impact of Suicide on Relatives and Friends*

After I lost my little brother, I heard a lot of remarks from people sharing condolences expressed with the best of intentions. "I don't understand," or "He was so young," or "He had so much to live for."

Most people simply asked, "Why?"

I didn't know how to answer.

The morning I received the call that he was gone, I can't say I was surprised. Pain, sadness, confusion and panic—yes. But not shock or surprise. I think deep down I always knew this was how I would lose him. Watching him battle depression was a family affair. We rejoiced during his highs but held our breath knowing the low was coming next. We suffered along with him.

When the effects of depression and mental illness are kept silent, it wins. Suicide isn't always an act of weakness. As survivors, we grieve, but learn to be grateful that our loved one held on as long as they could. Holding on more for us than for themselves.

No, I wasn't surprised. Perhaps . . . relieved.

The dictionary defines relief as "a feeling of reassurance and relaxation following release from anxiety or distress." Relief may not be the word people think of when faced with the sudden loss of a loved one. It might even seem a bit cruel to suggest such a thing out loud. Even so, I felt a sense of relief mingled with my depth of grief.

An important thing to remember is that David was not selfish. My brother's mind was his greatest asset and his greatest liability. He was not weak. He was a fighter. He was strong—

stronger than any of us who ask "why." I'm grateful for the 26 years he gave us. I'm proud he fought courageously for the 9,490 days we had with him.

But the people I am most proud of are my parents. The morning he left us there was a brief pause, the slightest hesitation, as to how we would handle the "hows" and "whys" concerning his death. My parents made the courageous choice to tell the truth about David's life.

*"Sometimes even to live is an act of courage." Seneca*

It has taken me the last five years to collect my thoughts on the loss of David by his own hand and I have come to understand one thing: Be thankful.

- Be thankful that your smile is genuine.
- Be thankful that you can feel.
- Be thankful that you are not suffering from this illness.
- Be thankful that you can look in a mirror and not hate what you see.
- Be thankful that you don't live in a mind that torments you.
- Be thankful that you don't know "why."
- Be thankful that you don't understand what it feels like to sit awake all night staring at the wall, feeling like you have run out of tears.
- Be thankful that you don't live for days, months, and years with no hope.

If telling David's story through this book helps just one person who has lost a loved one to suicide or inspires someone battling depression and suicidal thoughts to courageously choose life, then it has been worth every tear I've shed.

**A Gift from a Friend**

Meaghan Fisher befriended Amanda and the Lord family a couple of years after David's passing. During that time, she learned of his many loves in life, in addition to the many struggles he wrestled with. "My heart ached for them once I fully understood," she wrote. "It was obvious that his parents and sisters longed to know that he was at peace, even happy."

One day she discovered an Eskimo Proverb that inspired her to honor David in the hope of bringing comfort to his family: "Perhaps they are not stars in the sky but rather openings where our loved ones shine down to let us know they are happy."

# Star Name Deed

Be it known to all that this star, designated in the scientifically renowned Star-Name-Registry© as:

## 6409232 - Corona Australis

Residing in the boundaries of the above constellation is hereby named:

*David John Lord - 3rd October 2018*

The star's astronomically verified position is:

*Right ascension 19h 15m 7.21s*

*Declination -39° 34' 12.71"*

Magnitude 11.0130000

The public record is listed in the Star-Name-Registry©
and is copyrighted with the British government.
A duplicate of the star name deed is maintained
in a secure location.

*In memory*

On, what would have been, his 30th birthday, Meaghan registered David Lord as a namesake star located in the Corona Australis.

From bird watching to Doctor Who you were
right by my side when I needed you

*Dawson Coyle*

# David's Song
## By Dawson Coyle

Dawson learned all about birds and butterflies and how to see God in Creation from his apt teacher, David Lord. Throughout Dawson's elementary years, David impacted his homeschool academics with frequent memorable forays into the nature preserve treasuries of Southern New Jersey.

Dawson and David shared a passion for all things Dr. Who, too. Playing big brother/little brother, they enjoyed many hours debating the fantastic ins and outs of the Dr. Who story-world.

David's brilliance in theatrical activities also inspired Dawson in his pursuit of stage and performance, which he follows on his career path as a singer/songwriter, today.

In his original composition, *You Were There for Me*, Dawson sings a tribute to his friend and fellow bird enthusiast. The lyrics are published here for the first time. You can see and hear Dawson perform the song on his YouTube Channel at http://bit.ly/2PbdP1j.

## You Were There for Me

When I wake up and see the birds flying by
It reminds me of all the time we had together
You taught me to notice to seek and to find
The beauty you see in every simple feather

160

From bird watching to doctor who
You were right by my side when I needed you.
And You were there for me. You were there for me
I was way too young so what could I do
I never knew that you were hurting too
But you were there for me. You were still there for me.
I remember the night I got the news
I was broken and shattered inside
I didn't know what to do.
Even though you're gone it's not the end
I know I'll see you again my friend

I wish you knew how much you meant to everyone you knew.
You were my friend when I had none
So now this one's for you
I wear a smile right on my face
With air inside my lungs
My heart beats loud inside my chest
My feet stomp like a drum

From bird watching to Doctor Who you were right by my side when I needed you
And you were there for me. You were there for me
I'm older now I know what to do—I'll be right there when you need me too, and
I'll be there for you.
I'll be there for you

You taught me to notice to seek and to find
the beauty you see in every simple feather . . .

*Dawson Coyle*
*You Were There for Me*

# Cape May Bird Observatory

## New Jersey Audubon
### www.birdcapemay.org

*David Lord . . . one of Cape May Bird Observatory's stellar volunteer Associate Naturalists*

*Deborah Shaw*

# New Jersey Audubon Cape May Bird Observatory:
## Remembering David on the Trail
### By Deborah Shaw
### Cape May Bird Observatory

David loved nature. That was obvious, but I think even more, he loved his fellow man/woman. Not only were his skills as a naturalist remarkable for one so young, but his need to share them with everyone he met were of utmost importance. He sensed the quiet ones, those in the background that were shy and afraid to ask questions. He put them at ease with his own quiet demeanor. A very important skill for an educator. That trait served him well as one of Cape May Bird Observatory's stellar volunteer Associate Naturalists.

One of my favorite memories of David was during a back-bay boat trip aboard the Osprey, (on which I was a lucky participant) where he was a regular leader "working" to share the natural riches of the salt marsh with all the attendees. Nothing escaped his sharp eyes and ears. Not satisfied with just naming a bird, he proceeded to tell us everything about that bird and answer every single question with unlimited patience. His focus and intensity were impressive. He was in his element. It was a joy to experience and I will always remember that day.

### About the CMBO

Founded in 1976 by New Jersey Audubon, the Cape May Bird Observatory (CMBO) is a leader in research, environmental education, bird conservation, and recreational birding activities.

CMBO fulfills New Jersey Audubon's twofold mission to connect people to nature and steward the nature of today for the people of tomorrow in several special ways.

First, embedded in the DNA of CMBO, is our charge of keeping our finger on the pulse of migration. We do this through annual counts and censuses of wildlife, starting with the Cape May Hawkwatch in 1976, and including the Monarch Monitoring Project (est. 1990), the Avalon Seawatch (est. 1993) and the Morning Flight Songbird Count (est. 2003), and a host of other conservation-driven studies.

Second, we are training the conservation leaders of tomorrow, today, through our seasonal internships, George Myers Naturalist position, and year-round Associate Naturalist programs. Previous interns have gone on to run non-profit organizations, become community leaders in environmental justice, and to carry the torch of spreading the conservation ethic to future generations.

Finally, because we are located a tank of gas from 60 million people, we throw a great party to raise awareness for wildlife and wildlife habitat conservation! Our flagship festivals, the Cape May Fall Festival and Cape May Spring Festival, bring thousands of visitors to Cape May each year to celebrate the magic of migration at one of the greatest migration hotspots on earth! Each May our World Series of Birding engages over 300 participants from all over the world and raises hundreds of thousands of dollars for bird conservation, while highlighting the amazing diversity of birds across the Garden State.

Funded almost entirely by the support of an international membership, two facilities serve our members' needs and interests.

There are few places in North America which have been birded longer or have more birding advocates than Cape May, New Jersey, one of the planet's most celebrated migratory junctions. An array of habitat types and a wealth of protected natural areas make Cape May and the entire Delaware Bayshore a birding destination for all seasons. Wind and geography conspire to direct millions of migrating hawks, seabirds, shorebirds, songbirds, butterflies, and dragonflies here every autumn.

Friends of David and the CMBO share a few memories of this remarkable young man and the lasting impression he made in their lives. Many thanks to Peter Dunne, Pat Sutton, and Captain Robert Lubberman for their reflections on David's gifts on the trail.

# A Day Afield Marked for Greatness
## By Peter Dunne
### Founder of the World Series of Birding

In Cape May, NJ, a corner of the universe where stellar naturalists are not the exception but the norm, young David Lord stood out. It wasn't about his youthful exuberance nor the breadth of his knowledge, which was voluminous. It was his quiet intensity and dedication to passing his knowledge on to others that made David special.

Among the ranks of Cape May Bird Observatory's Associate Naturalists, David was singular. Any day afield with David was a refresher course into the wonders of the universe as seen through his discerning eyes and gilded by his unbridled enthusiasm.

When pairings were made for Cape May Bird Observatory's major events, all of us hoped to have David at our shoulder, knowing that the day afield would be marked for greatness.

Many leaders get lost in their role, consumed by the wonder around them, but David never lost track of his audience—a rare gift. He seemed to know intuitively when some member of the group was in need of his focused assistance. Field trip participants loved him for this. He was, in short, a leader's leader cloaked in a quiet, unassuming demeanor. The world is diminished by his absence, but his spirit and legacy endure in all who enjoyed the gift of his friendship.

## A Flame Burned Bright
### By Pat Sutton
### Founding Board Member of the North American Butterfly Association

David Lord was a great young man who developed a keen interest in the natural world. This abiding passion brought Dave into my orbit while I was Program Director for the Cape May Bird Observatory (CMBO).

Dave's interest in all things nature related grew and developed as he became more and more active with our organization. He eagerly participated in many butterfly and bird counts. Eventually, as his knowledge grew, he helped on CMBO bird and nature walks and field trips as an assistant naturalist. He gravitated to additional environmental organizations (CU Maurice River, Salem County Nature Club, and others) assisting them as well. Eventually, as time permitted, he worked as a naturalist aboard one of the back-bay birding by boat operations.

Dave shared popular nature presentations with the Salem County Nature Club and other organizations.

We all were caught by surprise when David Lord took his own life. We miss him dearly and daily and regret that he did not share his struggle with us so that we could have possibly helped in some way. Dave's flame burned brightly, but far too briefly.

# That Young Man Who Worked on My Boat
## By Captain Robert Lubberman

John Lennon wrote, "Count your age by friends, not years. Count your life by smiles, not tears"

Dave and I worked together on the *Osprey* birding boat, a wetlands tour of New Jersey out of Cape May and Millville, for five years. That Lennon quote reminds me of Dave. He connected with everyone. He smiled more than anyone I've ever seen. He touched more lives in his 26 years than most would in five lifetimes. I had the privilege of watching him enrich many people's lives over the years we worked together.

Even now, five years after his passing, people still ask about the young man who used to work on the boat and remember him for some connection that he made with them during their trip. These are not memories regarding his passing but memories they have of his living.

When he first started as the birding guide on the boat, he was not very comfortable working with the public, especially with young children. One of the things I remember is watching, over the years, as he learned different ways to connect with people of all ages. His excitement about the world we live in and the many subjects he enjoyed learning about really came through to people. I think that is why he is remembered so often by people who only met him a very few times.

For me and on the *Osprey* (pictured right, standing behind Dave and that smile of his), Dave lives on not just from the knowledge and the information that he passed on to the participants and myself, but also in the many stories and memories from literally hundreds of cruises we took together. If I included all of them here, we'd need to write another book.

*Photo Credit: Bottom right photo by Beth Freiday Ciuzio*

Like all enthusiastic birders, David kept a *Bird Book*, a small notebook carried on nature jaunts where he could quickly pull it out and jot down the bird, the date, and the place of a treasured sighting. The following photo montages are from his records kept in 2009 and 2010.

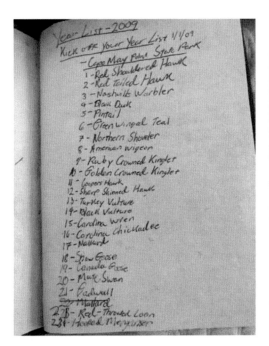
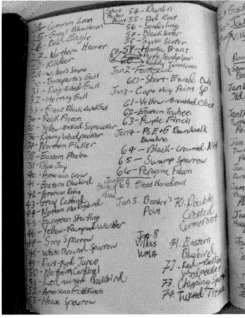

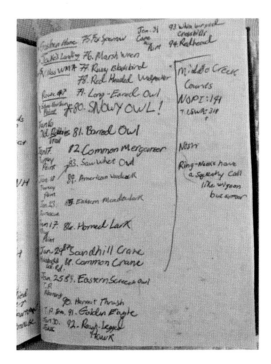
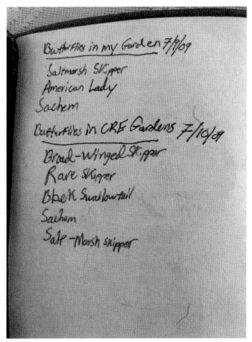

SEAWATCH @ 11/4/09 10:30-1:00
Seawatch 10:30-11:30

Black Scoter - 560
Surf Scoter - 250
White Winged - 6
Long Tailed - 8
Gr. Scaup - 6
Gannet - 40
SWWG - 3        11:30-12:30
BLSC - 1223
SUSC - 211
WWSC - 2
GrSC - 6
Bran - 3
                12:30 - 1:00
BLSC - 293
SuSC - 112
Gannets - 18
G. Corm - 1

---

11/9/09 Norgos at Meadows, perched at end
of Yellow Trail, seen from main trail
                                dune crossover
SWHA at Beanery - Winny Field
                        over shack
Going to Banding

Banding Saw whets on 11/9/09
    1st Check - 2
    2nd Check - 0
    3rd Check - 3
    1 bird got geolocator

Scouting ~~Sunrise~~ w/ Karen 11/11/09
Bald Eagles - Heislerville - 2    Veterans
            - Bivalve - 2              Day
            - Newport - 2      14 Bald
            - Husted - 2        Eagles
            - Greenwich - 2
            - Mad Horse -

---

Early Arrivals 2010:
Great Egret   February 24, 2010  Nimee's Beach
Wood Duck   February 22, 2010  Villas WMA
Osprey        March 4, 2010 Maurice River
Tree Swallow  March 9, 2010  Supawna
Forster's Tern  March 6, 2010  Villas
LAGU          March 6, 2010  Cape May Ferry
Cattle Egret  March 16, 2010  Seashore Academy
Purple Martin  March 16, 2010  Bayshore/Hampton
Pine Warbler  March 17, 2010  Belleplain
Eastern Phoebe  March 17, 2010  Belleplain
Little Blue Heron  March 17, 2010  Stevens Street
Blue Winged Teal  March 17, 2010  Beanery
Snowy Egret  March 19, 2010  CMBO CRES
Piping Plover  March 20, 2010  Stone Harbor
Least Sand. March 27, 2010  Meadows
Semipalmated Pl. March 30, 2010  Coast Guard Base
Louisiana Waterthrush March 31, 2010  Belleplain, Bridge
Yellowthroated Warbler April 1, 2010  Belleplain, Pine Plantation
Whip-Poor-Will April 2, 2010  Turkey Point
Glossy Ibis - April 2, 2010  Tuckahoe WMA
Whimbrel  April 1, 2010  Nummy Island
Willet     April 2, 2010  Reed's Beach
Clapper Rail April 2, 2010  Beanery
Blue Gray Gnatcatcher April 3, 2010  Belleplain
2 Black Skimmers April 5, 2010  Cape May CG

---

Green Heron April 6, 2010 Ocean City
Black and White Warbler April 6, 2010 Belleplain
White Eyed Vireo   April 7, 2010 Higbee
Pectoral Sandpiper   April 7, 2010 Paper Mill Sod Farm
Solitary Sandpiper   April 9, 2010 Stevens Street
Broad-Winged Hawk April 10, 2010 West Cape May
Ovenbird        April 11, 2010 Belleplain S.F.
Prairie Warbler   April 10, 2010 Triangle @ Belleplain
Northern Parula  April 11, 2010 Jake's Landing
Blue Grosbeak   April 13, 2010 Meadows

Thank You!

# Acknowledgements

## Chapter Contributors

We are grateful for the generous contributions of content made to this book project by some of those who knew David best in his many interests. We pray your willingness to support David in life and his enduring legacy *of* life will touch the lives of everyone who leaves through these pages. Thank you for your continued love for David and for the Lord family.

### Pastor Andrew Hughes

Andrew Hughes was raised somewhere in the murky swamps of South Jersey. However, his DNA links him to ancient English royalty and he demands that you treat him accordingly. When he's not enjoying the outdoors, Andrew is busy wishing that he was enjoying the outdoors. Otherwise, he may be found either creating a chapter-by-chapter video Bible commentary under the moniker "Bold Lion Ministries," or moonlighting as a karaoke superstar. He and his wife Stephanie currently reside in Naju, South Korea, where Andrew teaches English at a private academy.

### Jon-Mark Grussenmeyer

Jon-Mark Grussenmeyer and his brother, Timothy, befriended David while at Cumberland Christian School. Timothy and David shared the stage in high school plays, memorably starring together in Oscar Wilde's *The Importance of Being Earnest*. All three acted together as members of Kathryn Ross's Pageant Wagon Players for five summers of riotous melodrama fun, on and off stage. Jon-Mark obtained his MA and PhD in Medieval & Early Modern Studies at the University of Kent, Canterbury, where he currently teaches and lives with his wife, Grace. After teaching English in France and then pursuing postgraduate studies in England, Timothy and his wife, Charlotte, live in Vineland, NJ, where he oversees recruitment for Cumberland County College. Both count themselves blessed to have known David and are honored to be a part of this project honoring his life.

## Diana Hoffman

Diana Hoffman is currently working her dream job as an eighth grade English teacher in Bridgeton, NJ. She is also pursuing her master's degree and plans to further her education to include her doctorate in Educational Leadership. When she isn't in the classroom, Diana can be found either working on her historical home, hosting a tasty dinner party with family and friends, wandering Longwood Gardens, or pouring beer at her favorite craft brewery. Diana's friendship with David was a true gift and although there is still grief in the loss of him, she is grateful that his words can continue to inspire others and bring praise to our Sovereign Creator.

## Pastor Russell Sterger

Born and raised in Southern California, Russell Sterger graduated with an Associate's Degree from Bible College in June of 1995. He received his Bachelor's in Ministry from Trinity Biblical University in 2004 and his Master of Ministry in 2008. After graduation, he took on a position with Calvary Chapel Bible College in Austria, working as both administrator of the college and one of its lead instructors. Working with various mission-field endeavors, he served in Austria, Albania, Romania, Hungary, Uganda, Kenya, Sudan and the Amazon Basin of Peru. He served at the Calvary Chapel of Vineland as Associate Pastor and Administrator, in addition to oversight of the theatrical ministry of Calvary Chapel, The CCV Players. He passed on June 25, 2019 after a long battle with cancer.

## Pastor Frank Ippolito

Frank Ippolito was born in Chicago, Illinois in 1957. He moved to California with his parents in 1973, graduated from Katella High School of Anaheim in 1975, and devoted his life to Jesus in 1976. Since then, he has followed a life-long calling of service and pastoral ministry. He served as a missionary in the Alps of Austria for 6 years where he was able to see much of Europe, and is conversant in both German and Italian. Educationally, Frank has earned doctoral degrees in both Theology and Bible. He often travels to different countries to teach and has taught the Bible in different churches and Bible Colleges around the world. Frank is currently the Senior Pastor of the Calvary Chapel church in Vineland, New Jersey, where he has lived since 1998. He is married to his wife, Gerri, and has 13 grandchildren. He also serves as a chaplain with the Vineland, New Jersey Police Department and with the Cumberland County Sheriff's Department.

### Dr. Ronald Newman

Dr. Ron Newman is a licensed psychologist who has been working as a mental health professional in South Jersey since 1980. He directs the Christian Counseling Consortium of South Jersey which he founded in 1997 when he began his private practice. He has a passion for missions, having gone on annual mission trips since 1993 to do leadership training to pastors and church leaders, and is on the board of directors for the mission organization SALT (Support and Leadership Training). This chapter is culled from four articles by Dr. Ronald Newman, previously published in the Hammonton Gazette in 2017. Dr. Newman addresses various aspects of suicide—its varied causes, subsequent effects, and pro-active steps to greater awareness and prevention. Visit Dr. Ron online at www.drronnewman.com.

### Dawson Coyle

In 2017, Dawson Coyle made it to the Knock-Out Round on the popular NBC series, *The Voice*, launching his professional career as an inspirational singer and songwriter. His pop/soul musical style, thoughtful lyrics, and impassioned tunes present compelling messages of hope. He inspires multi-generational audiences to persevere through challenges, day by day, in both the valleys and mountaintops of life. You can hear Dawson perform the song, *You Were There for Me*, on his YouTube Channel at www.youtube.com/dawson-coyle/video

### Amanda Lord Wojcik

David Lord's older sister is married to Matt and keeps busy helping him run his businesses while managing their three young daughters. Her insights shared here in honor of her brother are beautifully expressed as they are compelling. Featured in her tribute is the David's Star certificate gifted to the family by a friend.

New Jersey Audubon
www.birdcapemay.org

### Cape May Bird Observatory

Many thanks to NJ Audubon's Cape May Bird in making the CMBO available for the public launch of this book. We encourage our readers to take advantage of the facilities for birding and wildlife education at the Cape May Bird Observatory in two locations: The Center for Research and Education, 600 Route 47 North, Cape May Court House, NJ 08210 and The Northwood Center 701 East Lake Drive Cape May Point, NJ 08212. https://njaudubon.org/centers/cape-may-bird-observatory

**Deborah Shaw**

Deb's interest in nature goes way back to a time when her grandmother's interest in birds and gardening rubbed off on her. Filling and watching birds and feeders and picking flowers were always highlights when visiting. Besides dogs and cats, horses played a part in her life for many years. Currently a small, backyard flock of chickens provides eggs and entertainment. Birds really gained greater focus when she began her job with NJ Audubon's Cape May Bird Observatory in 1998. Her favorite place to spend free time is her butterfly garden, or the woods, or on the Delaware Bay beach with her dog Graham.

**Peter Dunne**

For over thirty years, Peter Dunne has sought out birds in North America and has distinguished himself as a top expert in the field of birding. He has authored many books on the subject of birding, identification, and natural history. He is a familiar face in Southern New Jersey, serving as a past director of the NJ Audubon Cape May Bird Observatory, going on to be founder of the World Series of Birding. Peter Dunne is the 2001 Recipient of the Roger Tory Peterson Award from the American Birding Association for lifetime achievement in promoting the cause of birding. David Lord was honored to know him as a birding mentor in his life and his contribution to this book is greatly appreciated.

**Pat Sutton**

Pat's connection to the study of birds and butterflies in Southern New Jersey and beyond has spanned four decades. She has worked as a naturalist for the Cape May Point State Park and served 21 years at the New Jersey Audubon's <u>Cape May Bird Observatory</u> as Naturalist and Program Director. She earned a Master's Degree from Rowan University in Environmental Education and an undergraduate degree in Literature from the State University of New York at Oneonta. Pat has coauthored (with her husband Clay) many books on birds and butterflies including *Birds & Birding at Cape May* in 2006 from Stackpole Books. She is a Founding Board Member of the North American Butterfly Association, free-lance writer, photographer, naturalist, educator, wildlife habitat/conservation gardening champion, lecturer, and tour leader. Visit www.patsuttonwildlifegarden.com to learn more.

**Captain Robert Lubberman**
Robert Lubberman, A.K.A. Captain Bob, provides visitors to the teaming shorelines of Southern New Jersey with birding excursions through *Birding by Boat on the Osprey*. His cruises from the Miss Chris Marina in Cape May since 1994, access to marine life and birds in Cape May Harbor and Inlet, in addition to the coastal salt marsh of Cape May. Visit www.ospreycruise.com.

## Book Production

**Kathryn Ross, Editor and Compiler**
Miss Kathy ignites a love of literature, and learning as a family, through story and drama. Inspired by the stillness of birdsong, silent reflection, antiques, and teatime, she filters her love of history, classic literature, and the arts through God's Word, to inform her words. She is the owner of Pageant Wagon Publishing, working as an independent publisher and book shepherd to assist writers to develop and publish their books; and the founder of the Pageant Wagon Publishing Young Authors Collective, developing writers and creative communicators, ages 8 through 18. Kathryn Ross mentors women and homeschool families through teaching programs in literacy, language arts, and Christian living topics. Visit www.PageantWagonPublishing.com.

**Editorial Review:** A special thank you to Janice Heck for her keen editor's eye and recommendations in review of this manuscript. Thanks also to members of the Cumberland County Community Church Christian Writers Critique Group for their advice, brainstorming of ideas, and encouragement in the completion of this book and its goals.

**Prayer Warriors, Proofreaders, Precious Friends and Beta Readers:** Many thanks to Debbie Dilworth, Connie Jones, Missy Lord, Susan Seabrook, Gloria Watson, Debbie Weber, Judy Davis, Mark Gephardt, Edward Ross, Bethany Mathie (pictured with David on page 170), Deborah Shaw, Tabatha Scheffler, and Diana Hoffman for their generous time donated to pray for this venture and read through varied draft manuscripts to give helpful feedback towards a polished final publication. Special thanks to David and Kathy Coyle and our Calvary Chapel Vineland family for their prayers and support.

**Photography:** Unless otherwise noted, all the photos in the devotional sections of the book were taken by David Lord. Contributor head shots and random candid images are from the contributor and the collections of the David and Catherine Lord family, Kathryn Ross, Jon-Mark Grussenmeyer, David Coyle, Frank Ippolito, and Violet Brown Photography

**Special Credit:**
Kevin Karlson, wildlife photographer, generously donated the photo of the Red-winged Blackbird on page 42, in place of David's original, which was too dark for print quality. *"I loved David, and I am honored to share these for his book."* KK

Many thanks to Sophie Gabriella Photography for special graphics.

Many thanks to Veronica Diaz of Veronica Raquel Photography for permission to use some of her original photographs from the Pageant Wagon Productions melodrama years and memes created in honor of her friend, David Lord.

For information on commissioned paintings by artist, Noah Brown, whose work is featured in David's story, *Perpetually Perfect,* on page 84, contact by email: bynoahbrown@gmail.com

**Special Mention**

**The Pageant Wagon Players**
Upon announcement of this book project, we received cheers of encouragement from David's melodrama cast mates, the Pageant Wagon Players 2005-2009. Many thanks to you all for the cherished memories made:

The cast photo from the 2009 PWP Old-Fashioned American Melodrama Summer Family Theatre production of *Showstoppers at Starr's Theatrical Emporium* or "The Villain Vaudevillians"— David gave a memorable performance as resident comedian Aloysius Droll. Back Row L-R: Kathryn Ross, Director, Hannah Bradham, David Lord, Jacob Havens, Edward Ross, "Just Desserts" Bar Host; Front Row L-R: Liz Diaz, Jon-Mark Grussenmeyer, Tim Grussenmeyer, Bethany Finn Mathie, Veronica Diaz, Diana Hoffman; Kneeling: Nathan Havens. Photo by Veronica Raquel Photography. Not pictured: Ben Berry and Katie Weber.

*Veronica Raquel Photography*
*Veronica Diaz*

# The Last Word

The
Life of
Christ
is the
presence
of
God
in
us...

## Who Am I?

I am the salt of the earth (Matt 5:13)

I am the light of the world (Matt 5:14)

I am a child of God (John 1:12)

I am a part of the true vine, a channel of Christ's life (John 15:1,5)

I am chosen and appointed by Christ to bear His truth (John 15:16)

I am a slave of righteousness (Rom 6:18)

I am enslaved to God (Rom 6:22)

I am a son of God; God is spiritually my Father (Romans 8:14-15; Gal 3:26; 4:6)

I am a joint heir with Christ, sharing His inheritance with Him (Rom 8:17)

I am a temple - a dwelling place - of God. His spirit and His life dwell in me (1 Cor. 3:16, 6:19)

I am united to the Lord and am one spirit with Him (1 Cor 6:17)

I am a member of Christ's body (1 Cor 12:27; Eph 5:30)

I am a new creation (2 Cor 5:17)

I am reconciled to God and am a minister of reconciliation (2 Cor. 5:18,19)

I am a son of God and one in Christ (Gal 3:26-28)

I am an heir of God since I am a son of God (Gal 4:6-7)

I am a saint (1 Cor 1:2; Eph 1:1; Phil 1:1; Col 1:2)

I am God's workmanship - His handiwork - born anew in Christ to do His work (Eph 2:10)

I am a fellow citizen with the rest of God's family (Eph 2:19)

I am a prisoner of Christ (Eph 3:1; 4:1)

The greatest determinants of mental and emotional health are a true knowledge of God, an acceptance of His ways and the assurance of His forgiveness.

Excerpts from the Devotional Journal of David Lord, 2009

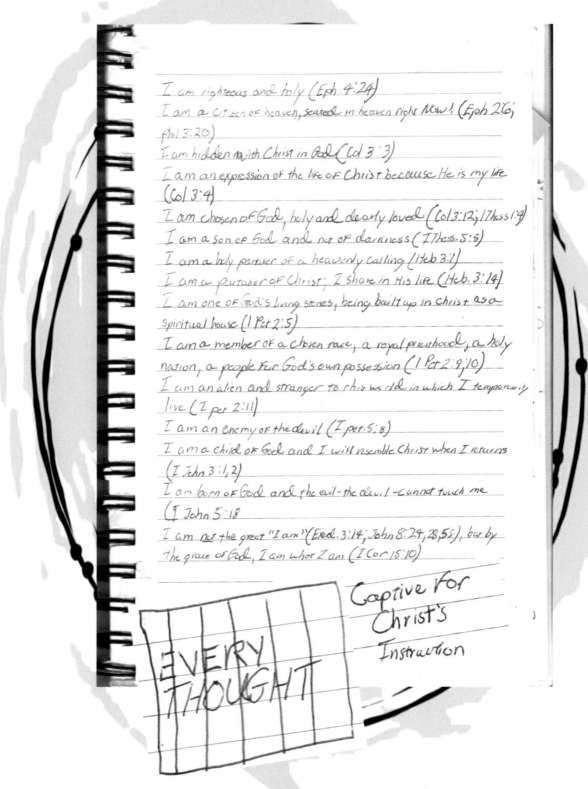

I am righteous and holy (Eph 4:24)

I am a citizen of heaven, seated in heaven right NOW! (Eph 2:6; Phil 3:20)

I am hidden with Christ in God (Col 3:3)

I am an expression of the life of Christ because He is my life (Col 3:4)

I am chosen of God, holy and dearly loved (Col 3:12; 1Thess 1:4)

I am a son of God and not of darkness (1Thess 5:5)

I am a holy partner of a heavenly calling (Heb 3:1)

I am a partaker of Christ; I share in His life (Heb. 3:14)

I am one of God's living stones, being built up in Christ as a spiritual house (1 Pet 2:5)

I am a member of a chosen race, a royal priesthood, a holy nation, a people for God's own possession (1 Pet 2:9,10)

I am an alien and stranger to this world in which I temporarily live (1 pet 2:11)

I am an enemy of the devil (1 pet. 5:8)

I am a child of God and I will resemble Christ when I returns (1 John 3:1,2)

I am born of God and the evil—the devil—cannot touch me (1 John 5:18

I am not the great "I am" (Exod. 3:14; John 8:24, 28, 58), but by the grace of God, I am what I am (1 Cor 15:10)

EVERY THOUGHT

Captive for Christ's Instruction

*Excerpts from the Devotional Journal of David Lord, 2009*

And I smile, knowing that, one day, that intrepid traveler will greet me once again with a vigorous, "Bonjour!"

*Jon-Mark Grussenmeyer*

182

183

Made in the USA
Middletown, DE
20 September 2019